The Joy of Thinking:
The Beauty and Power
of Classical
Mathematical Ideas
Part I

Edward B. Burger, Ph.D.,
Michael Starbird, Ph.D.

THE TEACHING COMPANY ®

PUBLISHED BY:

THE TEACHING COMPANY
4151 Lafayette Center Drive, Suite 100
Chantilly, Virginia 20151-1232
1-800-TEACH-12
Fax—703-378-3819
www.teach12.com

ISBN 1-56585-770-4

Edward B. Burger, Ph.D.

Professor of Mathematics and Chair,
Department of Mathematics and Statistics, Williams College

Edward Burger is Professor of Mathematics and Chair of the Department of Mathematics and Statistics at Williams College. He graduated Summa Cum Laude from Connecticut College in 1985 where he earned a B.A. with distinction in mathematics. He received his Ph.D. in mathematics from The University of Texas at Austin in 1990. In 1990, he joined the faculty at the Mathematics Department at Williams College. For the academic year 1990–1991, he was a Postdoctoral Fellow at the University of Waterloo in Canada. During his sabbatical years 1994–1995; 1998–1999; and 2002–2003 he was the Stanislaw M. Ulam Visiting Professor of Mathematics at the University of Colorado at Boulder.

In 1987, Professor Burger received the Le Fevere Teaching Award at The University of Texas at Austin. He received the 2000 Northeastern Section of the Mathematical Association of America Award for Distinguished College or University Teaching of Mathematics, and in 2001, he received the Mathematical Association of America Deborah and Franklin Tepper Haimo National Award for Distinguished College or University Teaching of Mathematics. In 2003, he received the Residence Life Academic Teaching Award at the University of Colorado at Boulder. Burger was named the 2001-2003 George Polya Lecturer by the Mathematical Association of America. He was also the 2001 Genevieve W. Gore Distinguished Resident at Westminster College and the 2001 Cecil and Ida Green Honors Professor at Texas Christian University.

Burger's research interests are in number theory, and he is the author of over 25 papers appearing in scholarly journals. He is the author of several books. Together with Michael Starbird, he co-authored *The Heart of Mathematics: An invitation to effective thinking* which won a 2001 Robert W. Hamilton Book Award. He also published *Exploring the Number Jungle: A journey into diophantine analysis*, and, with Robert Tubbs, co-authored *Making Transcendence Transparent: An intuitive approach to classical transcendental number theory*. He has also authored five virtual video CD-ROM textbooks with Thinkwell. Burger has served as Chair on various national program committees for the Mathematical Association of

America; serves as Associate Editor of the *American Mathematical Monthly* and a referee for many mathematical journals; and was a member of the Committee on Committees for the American Mathematical Society.

Professor Burger is a noted speaker and has given over 300 lectures around the world. His lectures range from keynote addresses at international mathematical conferences in Canada, France, Hungary, Japan, and the United States; to mathematical colloquia and seminars at colleges and universities; to presentations at primary and secondary schools; to entertaining performances for general audiences; to television and radio appearances including National Public Radio.

Michael Starbird, Ph.D.

University Distinguished Teaching Professor in Mathematics,
The University of Texas at Austin

Michael Starbird is a Professor of Mathematics and is a University Distinguished Teaching Professor at The University of Texas at Austin. He received his B.A. degree from Pomona College in 1970 and his Ph.D. degree in mathematics from the University of Wisconsin, Madison in 1974. In 1974, he joined the faculty of the Department of Mathematics of The University of Texas at Austin where he has stayed except for leaves as a Visiting Member of the Institute for Advanced Study in Princeton, New Jersey; a Visiting Associate Professor at the University of California, San Diego; and a Member of the Technical Staff at the Jet Propulsion Laboratory in Pasadena, California.

He served as Associate Dean in the College of Natural Sciences at The University of Texas at Austin from 1989 to 1997. He is a member of the Academy of Distinguished Teachers at UT. He has won many teaching awards including a Minnie Stevens Piper Professorship, which is awarded each year to ten professors from any subject at any college or university in the state of Texas; the inaugural awarding of the Dad's Association Centennial Teaching Fellowship; the Excellence Award from the Eyes of Texas; the President's Associates Teaching Excellence Award; the Jean Holloway Award for Teaching Excellence, which is the oldest teaching award at UT and is awarded to one professor each year; the Chad Oliver Plan II Teaching Award, which is student-selected and awarded each year to one professor in the Plan II liberal arts honors program; and the Friar Society Centennial Teaching Fellowship, which is awarded to one professor at UT annually and includes the largest monetary teaching prize given at UT. Also, in 1989 he was the Recreational Sports Super Racquets Champion.

His mathematical research is in the field of topology. He recently served as a Member-at-Large of the Council of the American Mathematical Society.

He is interested in bringing authentic understanding of significant ideas in mathematics to people who are not necessarily mathematically oriented. He has developed and taught an acclaimed class that presents higher-level mathematics to liberal arts students.

Recently, co-author Edward B. Burger and he wrote *The Heart of Mathematics: An invitation to effective thinking* which won a 2001 Robert W. Hamilton Book Award. A review in the *American Mathematical Monthly* (June–July, 2001) of this book said among much more, "This is very possibly the best 'mathematics for the non-mathematician' book that I have seen—and that includes popular (non-textbook) books that one would find in a general bookstore." He loves to see real people find the intrigue and fascination that mathematics can bring.

His previous Teaching Company course is entitled *Change and Motion: Calculus Made Clear.*

This course was made possible in cooperation with:

Key College Publishing, Emeryville, California
www.keycollege.com

Publishers of
The Heart of Mathematics: An invitation to effective thinking
by Edward B. Burger and Michael Starbird
http://www.heartofmath.com

Table of Contents

The Joy of Thinking:
The Beauty and Power of
Classical Mathematical Ideas
Part I

The Joy of Thinking:
The Beauty and Power of
Classical Mathematical Ideas

Scope:

Fun, joy, pleasure, aesthetics, intrigue, beauty, richness, texture, power, and life are words not normally associated with mathematics. In this course, however, we will discover mathematics as an artistic and creative realm that contains some of the greatest ideas of human history—ideas that have shaped cultures. We will explore the fourth dimension, coincidences, fractals, the allure of number and geometry, and bring these weighty notions back down to earth.

Every lecture will develop incredible ideas by starting from commonplace observations and building from there. By counting the spirals on the prickly facades of pineapples and pinecones, we will discover a number pattern that has a life of its own and expresses itself within paintings, architecture, and music. By tracing the edge of a twisted strip of paper, we will develop insights into the shape of our universe. By having monkeys randomly typing on a keyboard to create *Hamlet*, we will discover the underpinnings of molecular motion. Thus in this course, sometimes frivolous, inauspicious beginnings quickly lead us to fundamental insights into our lives and our world.

Mathematical thinking leads not only to insights about our everyday lives and everyday world, but also points us to worlds far beyond our own. One of the joys of life comes from playing with ideas that are not bounded by mere reality. There is no reason why our minds cannot go where no mind has gone before and live to tell the exciting tale. A mathematical point of view can take us far and bring us back home with a new perspective on everything.

Whether viewers already enjoy mathematics or frankly hate mathematics, these excursions will enable everyone to bring great mathematical ideas to life. The lectures will create a lively and entertaining intellectual *tour-de-force* that opens eyes and opens minds.

One of the obstacles traditionally associated with mathematics is its hierarchical structure. One goal of these lectures is to demonstrate that mathematical ideas are within the reach of people who may not have an extensive background in mathematics. The universe of mathematics contains some of the greatest ideas of humankind—ideas comparable to the works of Shakespeare, Plato, and Michelangelo. These mathematical ideas helped shape history, and they can add texture, beauty, and wonder to our lives.

Our exploration of mathematical magic and majesty will begin most appropriately with the contemplation of the notion of number. Simple counting will lead us to surprising outcomes and the discovery of an incredible pattern of numbers in nature. Unexpectedly, exploring this natural number pattern will take us directly to a geometrical realm that influences the arts and our notion of beauty.

With our aesthetics as our guide, we will discover new mathematical insights through architecture, art, and even in snails. Issues of grace and elegance naturally give rise to an exploration of the idea of symmetry. Looking for the most symmetrical objects is an age-old quest with a rich reward. We will appreciate these wondrous objects not only for their individual character, but we will also see their intimate, dual relationships with one another. Even the mundane soccer ball will become a richer object when we see it in a mathematical light.

The fourth dimension, at first, appears inexplicable and inaccessible. However here we will apply the lessons of mathematical thinking to penetrate the haze and look into a universe with the eyes of the mind. Indeed, developing intuition about this invisible realm is a rich example of the power of analogy and abstraction. The abstract notions of the fourth dimension can even touch our hearts and minds through the beautiful works of art they inspired.

As we will see, seeking beauty and surprise need not take us outside our world. A simple creation from a strip of paper will offer us a glimpse into a world of bending and twisting space. Our explorations will take us far beyond our own world and intuition as we rethink the basic notions of inside and outside.

Other objects of beauty can exist completely in our minds, but can only partially be rendered owing to the limitations of reality. We will discover that fractal pictures are literally infinitely intricate. They arise from repeating a simple process infinitely often, and they seem to capture the complexity of nature. Repetition is at the heart of fractals and perhaps at the heart of our natural world. Surprisingly, these incredible vistas will then carry us far afield to the birth of computing machines. In fact, the simple act of folding a sheet of paper will offer us a bridge from the wondrous patterns of fractals to the very foundations of all programming.

A final theme of this course is that much of our world experience involves chance and randomness. Although counterintuitive at first, we will see that amazing coincidences are nearly certain to happen to all of us. After thinking about chance and randomness, surprises appear in a whole new light. Randomness is a powerful force—it permits us to develop a feel for measuring our expectations about future events whose outcomes are based on chance. We will be able to see lotteries, insurance, and other games of chance with a more critical and informed eye.

As we will see through the course, the mathematics offered here will not remind us of school—there will be no formulas; no problems; no equations; no techniques; no drills; and no, there won't be any tests. Some people might not even want to call it math, but we will experience a way of thinking that opens doors, opens minds, and leaves us smiling while pondering some of the greatest concepts ever conceived.

One of the great features about mathematics is that it has an endless frontier. The farther we travel, the more we see over the emerging horizon. The more we discover, the more we understand what we've already seen, and the more we see ahead. Deep ideas truly are within the reach of us all. How many more ideas are there for you to explore and enjoy? How long is your life?

Lecture One
Great Ideas that Bring Our World into Focus

Edward B. Burger, Ph.D. and Michael Starbird, Ph.D.

Scope:

When we set out to understand our world more deeply, we start with our experience and try to see it with greater detail and nuance. A basic way to refine our worldview is to become more precise in describing what we see. We can move from a qualitative estimate of amount to measuring our world by counting. We can describe and explore the shapes we see. We can sensibly reason about the uncertain and the unknown. And we can go beyond concrete experience by expanding our inner world to include abstract ideas. Mathematics contains ideas and approaches that crystallize and extend our reach.

The classical theories of numbers, geometry, topology, fractals, and probability offer tools to help us better appreciate and understand our world. Each topic has surprises of its own and each illuminates the world through its insights and through potent strategies of thought that transcend mathematical issues. Mathematics is everywhere and can improve our lives if we embrace it.

Outline

I. One of the basic challenges of thinking, both for individuals and for society, is to understand our world more deeply. Lessons from mathematics can help us refine and expand our appreciation of the world. To deepen our experience of the world, we analyze it in several ways.

    A. We measure it and count things in it. We quantify the world.

    B. We identify and describe shapes and forms that make up our visual and physical impressions of the world.

    C. We deal with uncertainty and the unknown.

II. In each of these broad views of the world, mathematics brings us the light of refinement.

    A. For measuring and counting, we have developed the concept of number.

    B. To understand shapes, we have developed the mathematical world of geometry.

C. To deal with the indeterminate, mathematics offers the concept of probability to provide us with a quantitative sense of our uncertainty.

D. This course will follow these themes in three groups of lectures treating, respectively, number, geometry, and probability. Each of the lectures will present intriguing issues from each topic.

III. One of the sources of the power of mathematical thinking is that it allows us to go beyond our concrete experience of the world into abstract ideas.

A. One of the standard processes of mathematical discovery is to identify essential features of the physical world and reason about them in the abstract. This process often leads to new ideas in the abstract that are, in turn, reflected in the physical world. Our world seems to conform to the same logical coherence that underlies abstract mathematical reasoning.

B. On the other hand, if we view mathematics solely as a tool for understanding our world, then we miss one of its most fundamental features—its aesthetic appeal.

1. The beauty of mathematics arises from its conceptual elegance.

2. At first, this artistic side of mathematics may seem foreign, but we hope that you will come to view mathematical ideas as aesthetically pleasing.

3. The first place that we think about finding aesthetics in mathematics is in geometry. We will also discover relationships among numbers and amazing insights into coincidence and probability that give us the same sense of beauty that we get from a geometric concept.

4. We see an elegance of proportion and connection among ideas themselves, even when they have no geometric appeal.

C. Another attractive feature of mathematics is its timelessness. Mathematical ideas connect us historically with people from ancient times to the present.

IV. To whet your appetites for the ideas to come, we will briefly describe the outline of this course.

A. Lectures Two and Three will introduce the study of numbers.

1. Life is full of numbers. From the moment a baby is born, its parents record the date, the time, its length, its weight, and so on.

2. In the same way that numbers play such a fundamental role in our daily lives, they are also foundational in the realm of mathematics.

3. *Natural numbers* provide the tools for the most basic means of quantifying the world, namely, counting. We will find some startling possibilities in this mundane practice.

4. Natural numbers have captured the imaginations of people from around the world and throughout history. The study of natural numbers began thousands of years ago and continues with increasing vigor to this day.

5. To the eye of the mathematician, individual numbers have their own personalities and unique characteristics that differentiate each number from the others.

B. Lectures Four and Five will span the spectrum from number to nature. We will learn that numbers help us uncover hidden patterns and bring our everyday world into focus.

1. Often, we see beauty in nature because we subconsciously sense hidden structure and order. That order itself has an independent richness and beauty.

2. Hidden within the spiral pattern of a pinecone, for example, we will find the Fibonacci numbers. This simple sequence leads to both mathematical and aesthetic insights.

3. We will see that a powerful method of discovering a new idea is to isolate the pattern, then explore the pattern in its own right.

4. That journey into the abstract can inform our understanding of the world, which is sometimes fuzzy, even though we don't realize this fact.

C. The next set of lectures will move from the number world into the geometric world.

1. The aesthetic appeal of both the Parthenon and a musical composition by Debussy might be explained by a single underlying mathematical relationship.
2. Lectures Six and Seven open our exploration of the geometric universe by considering issues of beauty.
3. We will begin with a basic question of grace and proportions: What are the dimensions of the most pleasing rectangle? The answer leads us to the *Golden Rectangle*, famed for its recurring role in art, architecture, and music.
4. We might also ask ourselves whether aesthetics informs mathematical thinking or mathematical thinking influences aesthetics.

D. We then turn to other examples of classical beauty in Lectures Eight, Nine, and 10, as we explore the geometry that we learned in our youth.
1. If we had to select just one theorem to best represent all of mathematics, we might choose the Pythagorean theorem. In Lecture Eight, we'll examine three proofs of this theorem that span a period from ancient times to the late 19th century.
2. We also examine conic sections to illustrate certain basic definitions in geometry.
3. Lectures Nine and 10 continue this classical theme by exploring the regular or Platonic solids with their manifold symmetry.

E. Lectures 11 and 12 take us to a world that is visible only through the eye of the mind, the fourth dimension.
1. The very phrase conjures up images of science fiction or even the supernatural. It sounds, all at once, eerie, romantic, and mystical.
2. Because the fourth dimension lies beyond our daily experience, explaining and understanding it requires us to develop an intuition about a world that we are unable to see. Nevertheless, that understanding lies within our reach.
3. We'll learn that explorations of unfamiliar realms often begin by delving into the depths of the familiar.

F. In Lectures 13 and 14, we change perspectives from the fourth dimension. Here, we relax the rigid structures of both classical and abstract geometry and construct twisted surfaces that, amazingly, have only one side.

G. In Lectures 15 and 16, we'll move from the simplicity of folding paper to the subtle and surprising patterns of infinite fractal art and the concept of automata theory. We'll close these explorations with the realization that the simple paper-folding process is the key to unlocking the secrets of the beautiful fractal image known as the *Dragon Curve.*

H. Having examined simple geometric shapes and regular solids to this point in the course, we explore, in Lectures 17 and 18, irregular objects, such as clouds, rocks, and mountains. We'll learn that not all geometric shapes are elegant because of their simplicity. Fractals have infinite complexity and tantalize us with their properties of repeated self-similarity.

I. The third segment of the course takes on the challenge of probability.
  1. In Lectures 19 and 20, we will see how to describe quantitatively the level of likelihood that an uncertain future event may have.
  2. In Lectures 21 through 23, we'll learn how to measure the value of an uncertain future, discover the certainty in randomness, and explain the reason for the omnipresent life experience of coincidences.
  3. Probability and statistics enable us to better understand our world. They are the mathematical foundations for common sense, wisdom, and good judgment. We will explain how to place a value on decisions concerning investments, games of chance, and life insurance.
  4. Finally, we'll see that random behavior and coincidences do occur with predictable frequency.

J. The world is full of questions, interest, and surprises. Mathematical ideas and the mathematical way of looking at things can open our eyes to previously unobserved connections, insights, and wonder. We hope to show the joy, the creativity, the aesthetic appeal, and the wonder of some of the most intriguing ideas ever conceived.

Suggested Reading:

Edward B. Burger and Michael Starbird, *The Heart of Mathematics: An invitation to effective thinking*, Key College Publishing.

Questions to Consider:

1. Do you think that mathematics contains ideas comparable in philosophical and cultural significance to the best ideas and products in art, philosophy, music, literature, and history?

2. Do you think that the greatest mathematical ideas are genuinely accessible and intelligible to people who do not have extensive mathematical education?

Lecture One—Transcript
Great Ideas that Bring Our World into Focus

Ed: Welcome to *The Joy of Thinking*. I'm Ed Burger.

Mike: And I'm Mike Starbird. We've designed this course around two inextricably interwoven threads. There's a mathematical thread, and then there's this "joy of thinking" thread. You may well ask, "What does the joy of thinking have to do with mathematics?" The truth is that most people, when they think of mathematics, think of it as either unpleasant or as a rather rote process of following rules to solve for *x*. What makes us think that there's either joy or thought in that?

Ed: In truth, at the heart of mathematics, there are no anxiety-causing algebraic equations. In this course, we hope to offer up mathematics as an intriguing and creative endeavor. Our goal is to see mathematics as a joyful pursuit, that has within it ideas that stand among the greatest ideas of humankind, ideas comparable to the greatest ideas from philosophy, literature, or art. In this course, we will explore the foundational and basic ideas, the realms of number, shape, and likelihood.

Mike: We look forward to presenting what we consider to be so the most interesting and intriguing ideas that have ever been conceived any subject. Mathematics is often inaccessible to nonspecialists because of a couple of technical reasons. The first is that it uses technical terminology, and the second is that it is often presented using very cryptic notation that is impenetrable unless you have studied it and have figured out what every single little picture means.

I sometimes think that this habit of making mathematics inaccessible has ancient roots. It turns out that the Pythagorean society, which was created in 540 B.C., had as one of its tenets the concept of secrecy, that it discovered mathematical ideas and then kept them secret. And I have a feeling that somehow the mathematics community has never fully recovered from that habit. We hope that during these lectures you will encounter some really delightful surprises and mind-opening discoveries that will make you see mathematics as beautiful, important, and really effective at getting us to learn how to actually think better.

Ed: Part of that beauty of mathematics that Mike is referring to comes from the surprising connections that show deep structure with extreme elegance. Mathematics is obviously important to our everyday applications. We all know that, but here we will discover that its philosophical implications are also central to our culture. It actually creates a conceptual framework on which our understanding of many parts of our culture is based. Mathematical thinking is about ideas themselves, and the processes of creating them.

Mike: One thing that we all agree with, and I think understand about mathematics, is that it offers a standard of intellectual rigor that is probably the highest of any subject that human beings have considered. It also crosses cultural barriers, and it transcends the bonds of time. Mathematics that was discovered thousands of years ago is as true today as it was on the day it was discovered. In addition to that, though, it provides a way of thinking, a way of looking at things that can often augment, strengthen, and give additional vitality to every other kind of endeavor that we pursue.

Ed: That's why this course is about opening doors to new worlds of wonder. We believe that these ideas are individually fascinating, but together, they illustrate an approach to conceptual investigation that made these ideas possible. As we visit a variety of different mathematical domains then, we'll also observe a cumulative force in our strategies of analysis. In fact, one of our course goals is to present habits of effective thinking that can be applied to any aspect of life far beyond mathematics.

Mike: One of the basic challenges of thinking, both for individuals and collectively as a society, is to understand our world more deeply, and we believe that lessons from mathematics can help us refine and expand our appreciation of the world. We can learn to see more detail, we can see more structure, and we can see more beauty in everything around us. To deepen our experience and our understanding of the world, we analyze it in all sorts of different ways. One thing that we do is we measure it, we count it, we quantify it. Another thing that we do is to identify and describe the shapes and forms that make up our visual and our physical impressions of the world. A third way that we look at the world is to deal with the fact that we don't know what's going to happen— dealing with the uncertain and the unknown.

Ed: For each of these broad views of the world, mathematical thinking actually provides us with a light that illuminates what we see in greater detail. Thus, for measuring and counting, we've developed the concept of numbers. To understand shapes, we've developed the world of geometry. To face the unknowable future, we've developed the concept of probability that provides a quantitative measure for uncertainty.

This course will follow these three basic themes of number, shape, and unlikelihood (or likelihood). And both Mike and I will present intriguing ideas from each topic.

Mike: One of the sources of the power of mathematical thinking is that we can go beyond the concrete experience that we see in the world and expand our inner world to include abstract ideas. One of the standard mathematical processes of discovery is to find and identify essential features from the world, and then think about these, and reason about those ideas, and think about them in the abstract. This process often leads us to new ideas in the abstract that in turn reflect back into the real world, and make us see things in the real world that we hadn't seen before. Somehow, it makes us think that our world conforms with the same kind of logical coherence that underlies the abstract mathematical reasoning that we're going to present in these lectures.

Ed: On the other hand, if we view mathematics solely as a tool for understanding our world, then we miss one of the most fundamental aspects of mathematics, and that is its aesthetic appeal. The beauty of mathematics arises from its conceptual elegance.

At first, this artistic side of mathematics makes it seem foreign, or even meaningless, but we hope that you experience those "a-ha's!" of connection and insight, and will come to view mathematical ideas as we do, namely as aesthetically pleasing.

Mike: Certainly, the first place you'd think about finding aesthetics in mathematics is in geometrical insights, and that's true. In geometry, we're going to see really beautiful examples of aesthetic quality. However, there are also relationships among numbers, and for example, amazing coincidence and probability that give us this same sense of beauty that we get from a geometric concept. We see an elegance of proportion, and we get a kind of joyful sense of the coherence and the connection among ideas themselves, even when there's no geometrical content to them at all.

A feature of mathematics that I just love is its timelessness. Mathematical ideas don't get old. They connect us historically with people from ancient times to the present.

Ed: Mathematics is overflowing with fascination, and we hope that you will share in our delight in exploring the intriguing ideas we will offer in each lecture. Now, to whet our appetites for the journey ahead, why don't we take a little preview of the lectures to come?

Mike: I'll give a little enticement to the first two lectures. Suppose Bill Gates, in one of his better years, dropped a $100 bill on the ground. Would he be better off taking the time to pick it up, or to just keep working? The first two lectures beyond the introductory one, Lectures Two and Three, will introduce us to the study of numbers. Life is full of numbers. The moment we were born, our parents noted the time, our weight, our length; maybe they noted our width. I don't know, but they certainly counted our toes. Numbers measure things and count things. They accompany us throughout our lives.

In the same way that these numbers play such a fundamental role in our daily lives, they are also foundational in the realm of mathematics. In fact, that's where you think of mathematics first. The first thing you think of is numbers. We're going to begin at the beginning with *natural numbers*, the numbers that are so basic that they are called the natural numbers: 1, 2, 3, 4, 5. They are the ones that are used to count things. We're going to begin these lectures talking about plain old counting, and what we're going to find is that there are some startling possibilities in this mundane practice. For example, we will establish irrefutably that somewhere on Earth, there are two people with precisely the same number of hairs on their bodies.

Now, this insight is perhaps not what you were aiming for in a math class. In particular, it's interesting to note that this insight is not biological. It is actually a mathematical certainty that is based on counting and logic. The natural numbers have captured the imaginations of people around the world, and from different cultures throughout history. The study of those natural numbers, such simple things—1, 2, 3, 4, 5—began several thousand years ago, and continues with increasing vigor to this day. There are unknown questions about the simple numbers that people are continuing to explore, and to try to understand.

To the eye of the mathematician, individual numbers have their own personalities. They have unique characteristics and distinctions that differentiate each number from the others, and we are going to give you some sense of how it is that these numbers have those individual characteristics.

Ed: Numbers also allow us to uncover hidden patterns and to bring our everyday world into focus. In fact, after this course, whenever you're in a grocery store, and you look at the face of a pineapple, you will realize that you are actually looking at the face of mathematics. Why? If you look at a pinecone, what you will see on the surface are these wonderful patterns that form spirals, spirals that go in one direction, and spirals that go in the other. We will count them; we will count the spirals and discover something amazing. In fact, Lectures Four and Five will span the spectrum from number to nature and back again.

Often, we see beauty in nature, because we are subconsciously sensing hidden structure and order, and that order itself has an independent richness and beauty. Now, hidden within the spiral count of the pinecone, the pineapple, and the coneflower, we're going to find a number pattern that we are going to call the *Fibonacci numbers*. The simple sequence of numbers has a surprising structure, and leads not only to mathematical insights, but also to notions of aesthetics. It's rather hard to believe that aesthetics will come from numbers, but what we'll see is that a potent method for discovering new ideas is to isolate and abstract the pattern itself that we directly observe, and then explore the patterns in their own right.

Here, we will quickly leave the fruit and plant origins of the Fibonacci numbers, and dig into the *Fibonacci sequence* in its own right. Surprisingly, that journey into the abstract will inform our understanding of our everyday world, and you know, in some powerful sense, these explorations are going to be a wonderful metaphor for our entire journey through this course. We will discover that sometimes, we are unknowingly looking at our world in a fuzzy manner. Quite often, mathematical thinking allows us to see our world in a sharper way, where details that were once hidden now come into focus, and the beauty, structure, and nuance really shine through.

Next, we will move from the number realm into the more geometric realm, and the visual world, and so, I will start with a riddle. What do the following all have in common: The Parthenon, a villa designed by Le Corbusier, a musical work by Debussy, and the location of our bellybuttons? It sounds a little crazy, but the answer is that their aesthetic appeal might be explained by a single underlying mathematical relationship. Lectures Six and Seven will open our exploration of the geometric universe by considering issues of beauty. Now, our travels up to this point would have taken us to a sense of mathematical aesthetics, but here, we will actually wonder whether mathematics can be applied to illuminate the aesthetics behind art and nature.

Will begin with a basic question of grace and proportion, and we will ask the question: What are the dimensions of the most attractive rectangle, the rectangle that we envision when we close our eyes on a dark, starry night, and dream of rectangular beauty? That rectangle is actually referred to as the Golden Rectangle, and it's famed for its recurring role in art, music, architecture, and aesthetics. We will explore artistic works that reflected this mathematical notion from ancient Greece, the Renaissance, French Impressionism, and finally, to modernism, and we will be faced with the question of whether aesthetics informs mathematical thinking, or perhaps, more intriguingly, whether mathematical thinking actually influences aesthetics. We will explore the possibility of whether the aesthetic appeal of the Golden Rectangle may well arise from some elegant mathematical principles that actually generate those pleasing proportions.

Mike: We then turn to other examples of classical beauty, and I think of them as classical beauty because, in Lectures Eight, Nine, and 10, we're going to be talking about the geometry that we learned in our youth. But we're going to present it and, we hope, see it, as a field that is rich with a timeless beauty and real interest.

Think about this: If we had to select only one theorem that best represented all of mathematics, we might well choose the Pythagorean theorem. This theorem that talks about a right triangle—you remember that the square of the hypotenuse is the sum of the squares of the other two sides—was proved in about 500 B.C., or maybe even before that, and it captures an essential relationship between the sides of the right triangle. By this time, there are dozens or maybe even hundreds of proofs of this theorem that are known, and in Lecture Eight, we're going to see three examples of extremely elegant proofs. They span from ancient times to fairly modern times, one of them actually by President Garfield, who provided a proof for the Pythagorean theorem.

Among the constructs of classical geometry, the conic sections—where you take a cone, and you cut it with a plane, and you see the shape of the inner section—stand out for their attractive forms, and they have descriptions that you may remember, like: the set of all points, so that the distance from one point is fixed, is a circle; or that the sum of the distance from two points is constant, that's an ellipse. They have different ways of describing these different beautiful curves, and what we are going to show in this lecture, that the set of points for which the sum of the distances to two fixed points is a constant, is in fact the curve you get when you cut a cone by a plane.

Symmetry and regularity lie at the heart of classical beauty, and human beings have an instinctive affinity for symmetrical objects; that is, symmetrical things that can be turned or reflected, and they return to their original shapes, symmetrically, like the sphere. The sphere is the ultimate in symmetry. If we move beyond the graceful, constant curvature of the sphere, and we think about objects that have to have flat sides, then we can ask the question: How symmetric and graceful can they be? Well, that brings up the wonderful topic of the *Platonic* or *regular solids*. They are the flat-sided, symmetrical solids that have intrigued people for literally thousands of years.

Ed: Lectures 11 and 12 will take us into a world visible only through the eye of the mind, the *fourth dimension*. You know, the very phrase "fourth dimension" conjures up notions of science fiction, or perhaps even the supernatural. The fourth dimension sounds, all at once, eerie, romantic, mysterious, and exciting, and it is all of that. Physicists, artists, musicians, even mystics, all visualize the fourth dimension differently, and for different purposes. The mystique of the fourth dimension is alluring for all who contemplate it, as we will see.

Now, the fourth dimension actually lies beyond our daily experience, so visualizing it, exploring it, and understanding it requires us to develop an intuition about a world that we are actually unable to see.

Nevertheless, that understanding is within our reach. An important lesson that we will experience here is that explorations of an unfamiliar realm often begin by delving into the depths of the familiar. The fourth dimension provides a dramatic testament to the great power of developing a concept through analogy.

Now, while we will study the artistic works inspired by dimension, such as the works of Duchamp and Dali, we will also create our own art by actually building and visualizing a four-dimensional cube. Now, after constructing a four-dimensional cube, we will deconstruct it by unfolding its boundary to uncover, in fact, the inspiration for Dali's artistic work, and thus gain new insights into its meaning, so that yet again, we see that mathematical ideas allow us to better understand and appreciate what we see around us.

Mike: We move from the fourth dimension in Lectures 13 and 14 to changing perspectives a bit. In Lectures 13 and 14, we will relax the rigid structure of classical geometry, and even the abstract geometry of the fourth dimension, and instead, construct twisted surfaces that, amazingly, only have one side.

If you think about the surface of a ball, or the surface of a doughnut, or even the surface of a two-holed donut, the surfaces all have a property. They have an inside and an outside. If you are on the outside surface of a ball, you can't get inside without boring a hole, but we can ask the abstract question: Does every surface have two sides? To help us think about the two sides of this "sidedness" issue, we will build an actual physical model of a one-sided surface that's called the *Möbius band*. After we've held this Möbius band, and explored its endless edge, we feel a sort of eerie sense of oneness, that one edge, one side, one, one, etc.

We will explore it through various experiments, including cutting it up in various ways, and we find that the Möbius band stretches both our imaginations and our intuition. We can ask ourselves: Could we construct a one-sided surface that doesn't have any edge at all? Well, our attempts to make such a thing give us a wonderful model of how to take a simple, familiar idea, and create a new, abstract idea from it. We can effectively describe a very elegant one-sided surface known as the *Klein bottle*, and the neat property of the Klein bottle is that its inside is the same as it is outside, amazingly enough.

Ed: What if you take a sheet of paper, and start folding it again, and again, and again, and you keep folding it and keep repeating this? What you would end up with if you unfolded it is that it looks like a crinkled piece of chaos. In fact, though, there is hidden incredible structure in this jagged mess. Now, in Lectures 15 and 16, we will move from the simplicity of just folding paper, all the way to the subtle and surprising patterns of infinite fractal art, and the concept of automata theory.

Now, while the uninteresting endeavor of repeatedly folding a sheet of paper initially appears to be devoid of any intellectual offerings, here, we will soon discover that in fact, nothing could be further from the truth. By examining simple objects deeply, we suddenly uncover a treasure trove of hidden nuance and beauty, rich structure. Suddenly, out of the chaos, patterns begin to emerge, and the at first unpredictable randomness that we saw becomes completely understood and orderly.

Now, while these simple paper folding activities may appear to be just for those who are origamically challenged, here, we will make the intriguing discovery that paper folding, and its sequence, is actually an example of the classical computational theory of *automata*, developed by Alan Turing, the father of modern computing. In a surprising turn of events, we will then close our explorations with the realization that the simple paper folding process is actually the key to unleashing the secrets of the beautiful fractal image known as the *Dragon Curve*. Thus, we journey from paper folding to autonoma theory and to fractals by just following the thread of an idea and looking at simple things deeply.

Mike: Classical geometry is based on simple shapes: Circles, triangles, squares, cubes, and the regular solids that we will have seen by this point in the lectures. When we look at a cloud, though, or a rock, or a mountain, these objects are irregular. They have jagged edges. They're not formed by smooth and regular surfaces, and they don't really seem well described by the smooth and regular symmetrical shapes of spheres and triangles.

Clouds are complicated things. In Lectures 17 and 18, we're going to see that not all geometric issues are elegant because of their simplicity. Fractals have infinite complexity, literally, infinite complexity that tantalizes us with their properties of repeated self-similarities. Some artists are really known for their attention to detail. They produce pictures that are incredibly intricate, but only within the realm of mathematics can one create images that are literally infinitely detailed.

What does it even mean to speak of an image that is infinitely detailed? Well, the images that we are talking about can only be drawn to a certain degree of detail with the finest printers in the very finest ink, but the totality of their intricacy can only be fully present in the mind's eye. Every power of magnification of these objects reveals yet further detail. These are infinitely detailed images that arise from repeating a very simple process, but repeating it infinitely often, and then reasoning about the results. The beautiful images that we get really wonderfully illustrate the ideas of self-similarity, and a kind of symmetry that's just beautiful.

Next, we're going to discover that even random processes can lead to very specific pictures that have this infinite detail. It is surprising that something random can lead to a specific thing, and similar random processes give an alternative way to construct infinitely detailed images that can't easily be distinguished from actual photographs of the real world. In fact, there are theories about the stock market and even heart rate, that the kind of behaviors that are exhibited by fractal constructions are really at the heart of descriptions of those phenomena that we see in our everyday lives. Thus, we see that chance, together with some really simple rules, leads us to an infinitely intricate world of fractals, and maybe that fractal world overlaps with our own physical real world in ways that have not yet even been discovered.

Well, now we break. Our earlier lectures were about numbers and shapes, and now, we're going to face the third segment of the course, and that is to take on the challenge of probability. In Lectures 19 and 20, we will see how to describe quantitatively a level of likelihood that an uncertain future of it may have. If you think about it, many or maybe most of the significant events in our lives really arise from things like coincidence, and randomness, and uncertainty, just from chance. In these lectures, we're going to construct a means to measure the possibilities of an undetermined future.

To me, the idea that you could actually quantify the likelihood of uncertain possibilities of the future is an impressively grand idea. How can we sensibly give a measurement, a number, to something that we admit we don't know? Well, we use a technique of thinking that is so valuable. Namely, we're going to begin with some scenarios where chance dictates unexpected outcomes, but where we can list what possibilities there are, and then, we're going to show some really surprising things. But when the circumstance appears surprising, then that is a signal that we have to re-hone our intuition. We've got to proceed to develop the conceptual tools that help us to be accurate in our measurements of the possibilities of the uncertain future.

Thus, we will see other examples that illustrate the concepts of independence of possible outcomes and insight, that often, the best possible way to measure the probability or the likelihood that an event will happen is instead to measure the probability that it won't happen. We will see that if you have two independent things that both have to happen, then, the chances become slimmer that they're both going to happen, and we will learn how to see that the method to find out that probability is simply to multiply the probabilities of the individual ones. We will see why in these lectures.

Ed: Suppose you are attending a dinner party with 40 people. Do you think that two of them will share the same birthday? What are the chances? Pretty slim? Maybe we can never tell? Or, how about this one: You have a bunch of monkeys typing randomly at their keyboards. You think the one of them will eventually pound out *Hamlet*? What are the chances? Pretty unlikely? Who knows? Well, in the last three lectures, we will see how to measure the value of an uncertain future, discover the certainty within randomness, and explain the reasons for the omnipresent life experiences of coincidence. Probability and statistics enable us to better understand our world. In fact, they are the mathematical foundations for common sense, wisdom, and good judgment, and we will explore and explain how to place a value on decisions concerning investments, games of chance, life insurance, and see that sometimes, paradoxical situations actually arise.

Now, random behavior and coincidences do occur, and often, with predictable frequency. A bit of careful thought reveals that coincidences are not just as shocking as they may first appear. One of the most famous illustrations of randomness is the scenario of monkeys typing randomly at the typewriter. In fact, modified in terms of a popular expression, we see that, in life, *Hamlet* does happen. The theory of random walks is another theory that is counterintuitive and has surprising outcomes, and we will see reflections of it in *Brownian motion* and the stock market.

Finally, coincidences are so striking because, in particular, one is extremely improbable. However, we will come to realize that even more improbable is that no coincidence will occur. We will see that by chance alone, finding two people having the same birthday in a room of 40 people is extremely likely, even though the probability of any one pair having the same birthday is very low. If you were one of the people in the room having the birthday match, you would feel like something really amazing had happened, and in fact, something really had. Almost certainly, though, some pair of people with the same birthday will exist. Coincidences and random happenings easily befuddle our intuition at first, but we tame these ideas; we will see them in a greater light, and with greater understanding.

Mike: Well, the world is just full of questions, and it's full of interest, and it's full of surprises. Mathematical ideas, and the mathematical way of looking at things, can open our eyes to previously unobserved connections, insights, and wonder.

Ed: We hope to show that joy, that creativity, the aesthetic appeal, and the wonder of some of the most intriguing ideas ever conceived. Well, let's just begin.

Lecture Two
How Many? Counting Surprises
Michael Starbird, Ph.D.

Scope:

Life is full of numbers. The moment we were born, our parents noted the time, our weight, and our length and, most important, counted our toes. Numbers accompany us throughout our lives. Just as numbers play a fundamental role in our daily lives, they also play a foundational role in the realm of mathematics.

We begin with the *natural numbers (*1, 2, 3, 4, ...) and with the most basic use of numbers—to count things. Soon, we find startling possibilities in this mundane practice when we establish irrefutably that somewhere on Earth, there are two people with precisely the same number of hairs on their bodies. This insight is not biological; it is a mathematical certainty based on counting and logic. The compelling argument for this fact displays itself repeatedly in our daily lives, as well as in deep mathematical treatises; hence, it is referred to by its formal name—the *Pigeonhole principle.*

Outline

I. Our lecture series has two parallel goals: to present some truly intriguing ideas of mathematics and to point out and celebrate effective strategies of thinking that are beautifully illustrated by the mathematical way of discovering and developing concepts.

    A. We begin with the simple process of counting, one of the most powerful and fundamental ideas ever conceived by human beings, and the concept of natural numbers, which are building blocks both for understanding mathematics and for understanding our world.

    B. The concept of the counting numbers; the idea that for each natural number, there is a next number; and the notion that numbers can be thought of independently of objects are intellectual advances for understanding the world.

    C. One way to become a better thinker is to ask the question "How many?" in any discussion. That question forces the discussion to focus on quantitative measures of any issue.

D. The numbers that we use to make such measures are called the *natural numbers*, that is, the numbers that start with 1, 2, 3, 4 and go on forever. The most basic property of natural numbers is that they do go on forever; for each natural number, there is a next number.

II. First, let's talk about numbers with which we are familiar by virtue of understanding collections that contain them.

    A. We understand the idea of one, for example, as well as two's company, three's a crowd, and so on. We can take this idea up to 24 hours in a day, 28 days in a month, and 365 days in a year. These numbers are familiar because we deal with them all the time.

    B. But most numbers are much less familiar because of the property that every natural number is succeeded by another natural number—infinitely.

        1. To demonstrate the fact that most natural numbers are not familiar, we can show a 500-digit natural number that no human being has ever seen before watching this lecture. In fact, no one has seen a number within a billion of it or even a trillion of it.

        2. How do we know that no one has ever seen this number? The answer is that the number of numbers that can be made with 500 digits is so vast that even if every human being were counting numbers for every second of the age of the universe, they would still not even be close to this number.

    C. If we were trying to understand numbers by naming them, we would find that we would soon run out of names.

        1. Think of the numbers that we know that have names, such as *billion*, *trillion*, or even *quadrillion*. These numbers have just a few digits; they don't even come close to having 500 digits.

        2. The numbers from 1–9 have one digit. We can name numbers that go up to 12 or 15 digits, but then we run out of names.

        3. These 12- or 15-digit numbers are so small compared to the 500-digit number that they are almost nothing.

D. To get some sense of the various orders of magnitude and give meaning to large numbers, we can associate these numbers with familiar examples from our everyday experience. For example:

1. Right now, the population of the Earth is 6.3 billion, only a 7-digit number.

2. How many stars are there in the night sky? In the year 150 A.D., Ptolemy counted 1022 stars in the sky. In contrast, I was brought up in the bright lights of the Los Angeles area, and I never saw a star in the sky.

3. The number of meals we eat in a year is about 1000. The number of hours of classroom instruction in a standard college education ranges from 1000 to 2000.

4. The number of hours of work in a year is about 2000.

III. Getting into the habit of estimating quantities or finding the *order of magnitude* (a general size) for collections can put various ideas into perspective.

A. For example, the number of people in large cities is measured in small numbers of millions. The number of pixels on a high-resolution digital picture is referred to as a few megapixels (with mega meaning roughly one million).

B. Suppose someone offered you $1 million in $1 bills if you could carry it away. Will you be able to do so and get rich?

1. Estimating can help us answer this question.

2. How big would a stack of one million $1 bills be? We can cover one piece of paper with about five $1 bills. Two reams of paper stacked up, then, would account for $5000 and would weigh about 9 pounds.

3. One million dollars would be equal to 200 times our stack of two reams of paper and would weigh about 1800 pounds.

C. Let's think about billions by looking at Bill Gates, president of Microsoft. One year, his personal wealth grew by $20 billion.

1. If he worked 40 hours a week, 50 weeks a year, then he would work approximately 2000 hours a year. If he earned $20 billion a year, he was making about $10 million an hour.

2. If Gates saw a $100 bill on the ground, would it be worth his while to pick it up, or should he just keep working?

3. Dividing the $10 million Gates earns in an hour by the 3600 seconds in an hour, we find that he earns $100 every 0.036 seconds. He is probably better off to just keep working.

D. We hear a great deal about overpopulation, but if air and elbow room were not an issue, we could put the entire world population of humans, 6.3 billion people, into a cubic mile.

1. A linear mile is 5280 feet; a cubic mile is 5280^3, which is 150 billion cubic feet.

2. That area is sufficient to allow every person on Earth 2 feet × 2 feet × 6 feet of space.

E. The national debt is now $6.6 trillion.

1. Suppose a legislator presented a bill to pay down the national debt, claiming that this cost-saving measure would reduce the debt by $1 million per hour. How long would it take to pay off the national debt?

2. There are 24 hours in each day and 365 days in the year so, at a million dollars per hour, it would take about 660 years to pay down the debt.

IV. We can find several commonplace examples to illustrate how we can think quantitatively.

A. One of the ways we can understand how numbers grow is to conduct a simple experiment in folding paper.

1. We can ask what would happen if we folded a piece of paper 50 times. If we fold the paper once, it is two layers thick; if we make three folds, the paper is now eight layers thick.

2. Continuing to fold the paper, we see that each fold doubles the number of layers of thickness (four folds—16 layers; five folds—32 layers; 6 folds—64 layers, and so on).

3. Ultimately, after we have folded the paper 42 times, its thickness would reach almost to the moon and, after 51 folds, past the sun. This story serves as an example of *exponential growth*.

B. Another example of exponential growth relates to population growth.

    1. During the 20th century, the world population grew at a rate that was higher than 1% a year. Could that rate of growth be sustained for long periods of time?

    2. Suppose that at year 0, the world population was 225 million.

    3. If the population grew at the rate of 1.34 percent annually, after 2000 years, the population would be about 100 quintillion people (1 followed by twenty 0's).

    4. The earth has about two quadrillion square feet of land, so dividing the number of people by the number of square feet shows that, on average, every single square foot of land would have about 50,000 people on it.

V. Finally, let's use a method of logical reasoning to answer the following question: Are there two human beings alive today who have precisely the same number of hairs on their bodies?

    A. We can answer this question by reasoning through a proof to show that there must be pairs of people who have exactly the same number of hairs. This process, in turn, will show us a principle of reasoning that can be commonly applied in the world.

    B. We could first estimate the number of hairs on one person's body by closely examining one square inch of hair and coming up with an upper limit for the number of hairs in one square inch.

    C. We could then estimate the number of square inches on the human body by envisioning the body as a cylinder.

    D. If we multiply these two numbers, we would get an estimate of the number of hairs on a human body.

    E. We might then multiply that number by 10 to get an upper limit. In this way, we could reason that no one human being has more than, say, 100 million hairs. (In fact, we have far fewer hairs than that.)

    F. How does that fact guarantee us that there must be two people on Earth who have the same number of hairs? According to the *Pigeonhole principle*, with 6.3 billion people on Earth, all having fewer than 100 million hairs, we must have pairs of people who have the exact same numbers of hairs.

G. Other examples in which we see the Pigeonhole principle in action include the following:
   1. There are two trees in the world that have the same number of leaves.
   2. If we work in an office with more than 30 employees who arrive during the same half-hour period, two of them will arrive at work at the exact same minute.
   3. If we are in a group of 370 people, two are certain to share the same birthday.

VI. The step of quantification helps us understand every aspect of mathematics and the world.

   A. When we look at geometrical structures, we will find that counting and quantifying our observations will lead us to appreciate them more clearly.

   B. When we explore probability, we will see that putting a numerical value on uncertainty allows us to put some order even on randomness.

Suggested Reading:

Edward B. Burger and Michael Starbird, *The Heart of Mathematics: An invitation to effective thinking*, Key College Publishing, Section 2.1, "Counting: How the Pigeonhole principle leads to precision through estimation."

Questions to Consider:

1. Two thousand years ago, a noble Arabian king wished to reward his minister of science. Although the modest minister resisted any reward from the king, the king finally forced him to state a reward that the minister desired. Impishly the minister said that he would be content with the following token. "Let us take a checkerboard. On the first square I would be most grateful if you would place one piece of gold. Then on the next square twice as much as before, thus placing two pieces, and on each subsequent square, placing twice as many pieces of gold as in the previous square. I would be most content with all the gold that is on the board once your majesty has finished." This sounded extremely reasonable and the king agreed. Given that there are 64 squares on a checkerboard, roughly how many pieces of gold did the king have to give to our "modest" minister of science? Why did the king have him executed?

2. How do you know that in some year soon, more than 50 million people will die?

Lecture Two—Transcript
How Many? Counting Surprises

Welcome to Lecture Two, the first lecture in the section of the course that deals with number. As we outlined in Lecture One, the lectures in this course are grouped thematically into three broad categories associated with number, geometry, and probability. Lectures Two through Five form the Number Contemplation section. There are actually three sections on geometrical topics: Lectures Six through 12 form The Visual World of Geometry; Lectures 13 and 14 comprise The Amorphous Universe of Topology; and Lectures 15 through 18 will take us From Paper Folding to the Infinite Beauty of Fractals. The final section is called Measuring Uncertainty. Ed and I will each present lectures on each theme of the course. I will begin with Lectures Two and Three in the Number Contemplation section while Ed will continue on with Lectures Four and Five, in which he finds that nature herself seems to enjoy interesting number patterns.

We'll start these lectures by talking about the simple process of counting, because counting is one of the most powerful, most fundamental, most versatile, and most transformative ideas ever conceived by human beings. By the end of the lecture I think you'll agree with me that the simple strategies of asking "How many?" and doing some rudimentary counting, truly open doors for us to attain a clearer understanding of our world. And what I like about this topic is that counting leads to some memorable surprises. In fact, the title of this lecture is "How Many? Counting Surprises."

Before we get to these counting surprises, let me remind you that, as we said in Lecture One, our course actually has two parallel goals: one is to present some truly intriguing ideas from mathematics, but the second goal is to point out and celebrate some strategies of effective thinking that are beautifully illustrated by the mathematical way of discovering and developing concepts. We'll explore strategies of thinking that help us when we run into what appears to be a blank wall. We'll see how to open windows to see new vistas, and to build doors through which we can step into whole new worlds of wonder and insight. In a way, I like to think of this aspect of the course as lessons in what to do when we don't know what to do. And seeking a general idea of sizes—that is, having an order of magnitude estimate of quantities—often opens up possibilities for our understanding of the world.

For example, in the 17th century, Bishop James Ussher calculated that the Earth was created in October of the year 4004 B.C.—it might actually have been on Halloween. But in the 19th century, Charles Lyell argued that the Earth was millions of years old. Now we know that the Earth is a few billion years old. With millions or billions of years to work with, influences that seem modest, such as erosion, or events that are rare, such as earthquakes and volcanoes, suddenly have time to account for the creation of the geological features of the Earth that we observe; whereas if the Earth were only 6000 years old, a little annual erosion and the occasional volcano simply would not have time to make a significant dent in the world. So having a quantitative view of the issue completely alters our sense of what is possible or impossible.

From counting emerged the abstract concept of number and in that step of abstraction, humankind took a leap of intellectual development that is absolutely fundamental to our experience of the world as we know it today.

So during this lecture we will be talking about the *natural numbers* that are the building blocks both for understanding mathematics and for understanding our world in some really fundamental way. The natural numbers are the numbers that we use for counting, that is, the natural numbers are the numbers 1, 2, 3, 4, 5, and so on. The basic property of the natural numbers is that every natural number is followed by a natural number that is one larger. So this process of adding one more after each natural number means that there is no end to the natural numbers. The natural numbers go on forever.

But the numbers we ordinarily deal with are quite small, and we are comfortable with them through their association with familiar collections, that is, a small number means something to us because it brings to our minds several collections of that same size.

Let's start where the natural numbers start, that is, with 1. One (1), oneself, the idea of unit, but to be perfectly honest, historically speaking the number one was probably not viewed as a number until the concept of number had been developed. If one were the only number, we wouldn't even name it. To me there is a philosophical point here: Sometimes we don't really identify the simplest cases until we have understood more complex cases of some phenomenon. So let's move to the number 2.

Two (2), two hands, two feet, and if two's company, then three's a crowd. Which takes us to the number three (3): the dimensions of the space we live in, three is the smallest number of legs for a stool to stand up, three has religious significance with the Trinity, and its the number of toes on the foot of a three-toed sloth. The number four (4), nature provides exemplars of 4, lots of them. The number of legs on a cat or dog or other animals; the number of legs on a table, tires on a car; the number of people you need to play bridge or doubles tennis. Five (5), a very basic one, the number of fingers on each hand is five. It's so fundamental. Notice by the way, it's fundamental to our number system, but if you look around the world, five doesn't really come up that often except for the number of fingers on a hand, but because we see it every day, it's become central to our number system.

Six (6) sides of a die, seven (7) days in a week, eight (8) bits in a byte, nine (9) innings in a baseball game. Ten (10), ten fingers. Once again, the thing we see most often associated with numbers are hands and that is so familiar that it has become the basis of our number system. Other familiar numbers: 12, the number of eggs in a dozen; 20, if we count our fingers and our toes; 24 hours in a day; 28 days in a lunar month; 365 or 366, days in a year. These numbers are familiar because we encounter them all the time through their associations.

So we have a sense of some small numbers, but most numbers are really big and most natural numbers do not have human associations. In fact, most natural numbers have never been seen by human eyes.

To demonstrate this, I will now show you a specific number that no human being has ever seen before watching this lecture. In fact, no one has seen any number within a billion of it, or even a trillion of it. It's really just a random string of about 500 digits.

Different people react differently to the idea of seeing a number that no one has ever seen before. Some don't care. "So what?" they might say. And maybe that's the right reaction. Because actually since there are infinitely many natural numbers, there are plenty that no one has ever seen.

But I hope you might at least have some curiosity about why I think that no one has seen this number before. Might not someone in China, in the year 1300, have written down this very number?

Well, the purpose of this lecture is to take the trouble to count. So let's count. Let's suppose that someone set a very fast computer to count all numbers it could and that the computer was started at the moment of the Big Bang. Suppose this fast computer could count a billion numbers each second. Let's see whether that computer would have made it to the number on the screen. So let's just figure out how many seconds there have been since the beginning of the universe. The universe, we are told, is about 13.7 billion years old. Each year has 365 days, each day has 24 hours, each hour has 60 minutes, and each minute has 60 seconds. So the universe is about $13,700,000,000 \times 365 \times 24 \times 60 \times 60$ seconds old. Just doing the multiplication, we see that the universe is about $430,000,000,000,000,000$ seconds old. The thing to notice is that the number that counts how many seconds there have been since the beginning of the universe has only a few digits. It has only 18 digits.

If our computer counted a billion numbers each second, it would have counted $430,000,000,000,000,000 \times 1,000,000,000$ numbers, which just has 27 digits in total. Notice that that number is paltry compared with the 500-digit number we first saw on the screen. The number of combinations of digits to create a 500-digit number is so incredibly vast compared even to the age of the universe, that there's no real chance that it has ever been seen before. Even if someone gave us the first 470-digits of the number, we would still require longer than the age of the universe to systematically try the other possible combinations just to get the last 30 digits. And if we wanted a number within a trillion of that number, the number would have to agree exactly in every single digit except for the last 9 or 10.

To me it's fascinating to think that the total age of the universe in seconds can be written down with a number that is just 18 digits long.

So numbers such as that huge 500-digit number really have essentially no specific human meaning. The numbers we humans deal with are tiny in comparison.

But before we leave this 500-digit number, let's think about the natural numbers *in toto*. Remember that each natural number is followed by a natural number that is one bigger, then that number is followed by a number one larger than that, and one larger still, and so on, forever. In particular, there can be no largest number because if we thought we had a candidate for the largest number, the number that's one larger would demonstrate the error in our ways.

We only name tiny numbers, relatively speaking. Suppose your job were to name numbers. Just start naming numbers. When we have done the number one, we have infinitely many more to go. After we have named a trillion, we still have infinitely many to go. When we get to that 500-digit number, which as we saw would take many, many times longer than the whole age of the universe, we still would have just begun. That huge number itself is actually completely inconsequential relative to the size of most numbers, because infinitely many numbers are larger than that number while only finitely many precede it.

In our world a 500-digit number is without real meaning. But distinctions among relative sizes of pretty big numbers play important roles in our lives that were not present for our ancient ancestors and were not even important as recently as our grandfathers' day. With the advent of computers, we have become accustomed to thinking more commonly about numbers in millions, billions, and even trillions. Distinctions among these large numbers make a practical difference in our lives. And understanding the order of magnitude of numbers—that is, the approximate size of various collections—can give us some insights and put some parts of our experience of the world into perspective. How can we make sense of large numbers so that it means something to us when people talk about millions versus billions versus trillions?

The answer is to take these large numbers and connect them with everyday experience, just as we do with the tiny numbers from one to ten. So let's take some large numbers and tame them, that is make sense of them by associating them with some everyday experience.

In a fundamental way, the best way to understand anything is to associate it with ideas that are previously familiar. So let us get some sense of various orders of magnitude, that is, let's think of some examples of collections in the thousands, the millions, the billions, and the trillions and then do an exercise of understanding.

Let's start with a thousand. For a thousand, a good example is the number of stars in the night sky. In the year 150 A.D., the astronomer Ptolemy counted 1022 stars in the night sky.

Of course, this may not be a great example for people like me. You see, I was brought up in the bright lights of the Los Angeles area, so I don't recall ever seeing a star in the night sky. Stars were pretty much theoretical ideas for me.

Another example of about a thousand is the number of meals we eat in a year: 365 days times three meals a day, about a thousand.

Another example of one or two thousand is the number of classroom hours of instruction in a standard college education.

Two thousand is about the number of hours of work in a year—50 weeks times 40 hours per week, which is 2000.

So we have many familiar examples of everyday experience that make numbers in the thousands meaningful to us. Notice that we are not interested in being precise. For now we are just interested in how to get a sense of numbers so that we have a distinct difference in our minds when we hear thousands versus millions versus billions.

Let's move on to millions, because as we get to larger numbers, we may need to take some mental action to make those numbers meaningful. What can we do to make the number one million meaningful? Again, one way is to think of familiar collections that are measured in millions. For example, the number of people in a large city is measured in small numbers of millions. The population of states is measured in millions. The number of pixels on a high-resolution digital camera is referred to as a few megapixels, and mega means roughly a million.

But these examples may not give us a visceral sense of a million, so let's try the following mental experiment. How much would a million dollars weigh? That is, suppose someone offered you $1 million in $1 bills if you could carry it away. Would you be rich? Of course, your first reaction is: "I don't know if I could carry it or not?" But when we are faced with such a question, we might be surprised what a little thought can do. That is, you might be surprised how easy it is to estimate quantities and thereby, get a more refined sense of them. In this case, how would we estimate the weight of a million dollars?

Well, a good strategy is to take something related that is familiar and then make a connection. In general, making a connection between an unfamiliar idea and a familiar one is a good way to move toward understanding. In this case of trying to estimate the weight of a million dollars, we might start with a familiar paper object, namely, a ream of paper. Here are two reams, that is, 1000 sheets of paper. Each piece of paper is about equal in weight to five $1 bills, since five bills would just about cover one piece of paper. So the 1000 sheets of paper would weigh the same as about 5000 dollar bills. Well, a million dollars is 200 times as much as $5000. So a million dollars would weigh about 200 times as much as this stack of paper. But just hefting it gives us some guess about its weight—maybe 9 pounds. So 200 times that amount would be about 1800 pounds— close to a ton. So if someone offers us a million dollars in one's if we can carry it away, I fear that unless we have spent an awful long time in the gym, sadly, we would not be rich.

Let's move on to billions. For billions, perhaps the best example is the number of people on Earth. Right now there are about 6.3 billion people. Another example of billions is the age of the universe in years—13.7 billion years since the Big Bang. Or the number of bytes of storage on computers these days. A gigabyte means about a billion bytes.

These examples help us to understand a billion, but still they may not put the number in perspective. Here is a thought question that might help us to answer the question: How big is a billion? A few years ago, I read that in one of his better years, Bill Gates's personal wealth grew by $20 billion. Suppose he were an hourly wage earner, you know, like McDonald's only more so. If he saw a $100 bill on the ground, should he pick it up or keep working? This mental experiment will give us some idea of how big $20 billion really is. Well, let's just take the time to analyze this question quantitatively.

If Mr. Gates worked 40 hours a week for 50 weeks, he would work 2000 hours during the year. To earn his $20 billion, he would have to earn $20 billion divided by 2000 hours, which equals $10 million per hour. Not a bad wage.

Well, each hour has 60 minutes and each minute has 60 seconds, so there are 3600 seconds in an hour. So Mr. Gates earned $10 million divided by 3600 seconds or about $2800 each second. So he took in $100 every 0.036 seconds, that is less than four-hundredths of a second. The people with the fastest reflexes require about a tenth of a second to react. So not only would Mr. Gates not be wise to pick up the $100 bill, he would be unwise even to think about picking it up. He'd better just keep working.

To me that little analysis puts the concept of 20 billion in real perspective.

Here's another observation about numbers in billions that I think is pretty striking. We hear a great deal about overpopulation, but if air and elbowroom were not an issue, we could put the entire world population of over six billion humans into one cubic mile. This fact is easy to confirm. A mile is 5280 feet. So a cubic mile is 5280 feet long times 5280 feet wide times 5280 feet tall. So a cubic mile has 5280×5280×5280 cubic feet, which is about 150 billion cubic feet. Dividing 150 billion by 6 billion gives each person about 25 cubic feet. So each of us, packed like sardines, could have a space of about 2 feet by 2 feet by 6 feet. That image might be a little uncomfortable for claustrophobics.

Let's move on to trillions. There are very few numbers we actually encounter that are measured in the trillions. But among them, sadly, is the United States's national debt. In 2003, the national debt was about $6.6 trillion = $6,600,000,000,000

How can we understand this enormous number? Well, maybe we could approach it in terms of trying to pay it off. Suppose a legislator proudly presented a bill to pay down the debt and the legislator bragged that this cost-saving measure would reduce the debt by $1 million dollars per hour! Sounds pretty good—but just to make sure, let's count how long it will take to pay off the whole debt at that rate. Let's first just count how much the debt would be reduced each year. That's easy: there are 24 hours in each day and 365 days in the year. So at a million dollars per hour, we could reduce the debt by 24×365×$1,000,000, which equals about $10,000,000,000, that is, $10 billion per year. At that rate, it would require $6.6 trillion divided by $10 billion or 660 years to pay down the debt. Such estimation can help put debt reduction schemes into perspective.

We have seen some methods for starting with numbers—millions, billions, trillions—and making sense of them by thinking of some familiar situations that helped to illustrate those sizes. Let's now start with some everyday activities and estimate the orders of magnitude of the numbers that arise.

Here's a very simple experiment. Suppose we take a piece of paper and fold it, then fold it again, and fold it again and so on. Notice that when we fold these papers, we get twice as many sheets on each fold. For now, we're going to ask the question: How thick would the stack of paper be if we folded a sheet of paper 50 times?

As we saw, when we folded it the first time, we'd get two layers thick. When we folded it again, we got four layers thick; 3 folds—8 layers; 4 folds—16 layers; 5 folds—32 layers; 6 folds—64 layers; 7 folds—128 layers; 8 folds—256 layers; 9 folds—512 layers; and after 10 folds it would be over 1000 layers thick or 1024 layers thick.

So this stack of 1024 sheets would be the thickness of one piece of paper if it could be folded 10 times. At this stage, it's really looking pretty thick, about three inches thick.

In any case we can continue this progression of thicknesses, noting that the paper doubles in thickness with each fold. Notice that the folded paper gets thick quite fast. After 20 folds, we are taller than a 20-story building. After 30 folds, we are 50 miles thick which takes us into the upper atmosphere. After 42 folds, we are almost to the moon. And after 51 folds, we've gone further than the 93 million miles to the sun!

In later lectures, Ed will actually use this concept of paper-folding when he talks about fractals and creates an amazing curve called the *Dragon Curve*.

Let's apply this strategy of looking at situations quantitatively to understand something about the rate of population growth. Here are some facts: In the year 1900, the world population was 1.6 billion; in 2000, it was 6.1 billion. That growth corresponds to a growth rate of 1.35 percent per year. That is to say, for every 100 people alive one year there were 101.35 people alive the next year. Might that be about the historical average? What do you think? Well, here's a way to look at that question. Suppose the population had increased by that rate, the rate it did in the 20th century, since the year zero. How many people would be alive today?

Well, the population at year zero is estimated to have been about 225 million. If the population grew at the 20th century's rate, then after 2000 years, the population would be about 100 quintillion people, that is, a one with 20 zeros after it (100,000,000,000,000,000,000). To put that number in perspective, let's see how much room each person would have. The Earth has about two quadrillion square feet, that is, two with 15 zeros square feet of land (2,000,000,000,000,000). So dividing the number of people by the number of square feet available shows that on average every single square foot of land would have about 50,000 people on it. That cubic mile with all of humanity in it is beginning to sound pretty roomy.

So we can conclude that the 20th century's rate of population growth simply will not happen for long periods of time. In fact, it is extremely unlikely to continue at that rate even through the lives of our own grandchildren. Something has to give.

Sometimes estimation together with a little clear reasoning can lead to exact results. Here is a question that may seem a little bizarre. Are there two people on Earth with the same number of hairs on their bodies?

We won't count the number of hairs on anyone's body, but can we estimate how many hairs are possible? We don't have to be too precise. Let's just find a number that is so large that we can be certain that no person on Earth, no matter how big and how hairy would have that many hairs. Here's an easy way to estimate. No person is 100 inches around. No person is 100 inches tall. So even counting wrinkles, arms, and heads, no person has as much as 100×100 that is 10,000 square inches of skin. Just by looking at a little bit of hair on our heads, we can easily count that no square inch of hair could have anything approaching 10,000 hairs on it. So the maximum number of square inches of skin (10,000 square inches) times an overestimate of the number of hairs per square inch (10,000 hairs per square inch) gives a number that is clearly far larger than the number of hairs on any one person's body. That is: $10,000 \times 10,000 = 100,000,000$. That is, 100 million is larger than the number of hairs on any one person's body.

Now let's do some reasoning. Suppose we made 100 million rooms and labeled them with the numbers one, two, three, and so on up to 100,000,000. Now in our minds, we line up all the people on Earth, all 6.3 billion of them and one by one ask each person to step into the room whose number is the number of hairs on their body. Each person goes into a room. But what happens after 100 million people have gone into their appropriate room. Well, even if all 100 million people went into different rooms, there would still be a long line of people left who have to go somewhere. So after 100 million, we are absolutely forced to have a duplication, because they can't all be in different rooms. So it is the fact that there are more people than there are hairs on the body of any one person that guarantees us that there must be duplications in the body-hair count.

Now that we settled this important, hairy question, let's step back and cull from the experience a method of reasoning.

Actually, the line of reasoning we used is called the *Pigeonhole principle*. If we have 26 pigeonholes on a desk, for example, one for each letter of the alphabet, and we have more than 26 envelopes to sort into the pigeonholes, then we know for certain that some pigeonhole will have more than one envelope. It's obvious.

Once we see how this Pigeonhole principle works, we actually can see it being applicable to many questions in everyday life. I'll leave it to you to think of some examples to answer the following questions:

1. Show that there are two leafy trees on Earth with the exact same number of leaves.

2. If we work in an office with more than 30 employees and who arrive during the same half-hour period, then two of them will arrive at work at the exact same minute.

3. If we are in a group of 370 people, two are certain to share the same birthday. (Incidentally, in Lecture 23, Ed will show us a real surprise about birthday coincidences during our lectures on probability.)

In this lecture, we have seen how the simple act of counting can put aspects of our world in perspective. We should note that we have also seen the versatility of natural numbers. They can be used to count anything. Some of our Stone Age ancestors could count one banana, two bananas, three bananas…but only later conceived the abstract idea of separating the numbers from the specific things they were counting, thus creating the concept of numbers that could count anything. Of course, we take this flexibility of numbers completely for granted, but their universal applicability gives them an amazing property of versatility if we stop to think about it.

But the truth is that one of the main reasons I wanted to tell you about these examples is that I find them fascinating. To me it's just amazing that if you could fold a piece of paper about 40 times it would reach to the Moon and about 50 times you'd be to the Sun; or that during a good year, Bill Gates doesn't have time to pick up a $100 bill; or that if the population of the planet had grown at the rate it did during the last century for the previous 2000 years, there would more than 50,000 people per square foot over the entire planet. But these estimations do make a serious point beyond just the fun of the numbers; namely, taking the trouble to count puts matters in perspective. If we want to experience the world with more subtly, more precision, more detail, asking "How many?" is an excellent strategy to employ.

In this lecture, you will have noticed that we were content with estimates. We really just focused on approximately how many of various things we had. The specific numbers did not matter; in fact, in the examples in this lecture, we couldn't really find the specific numbers even if we wanted to—and we certainly didn't want to find the specific number of hairs on anybody's body. In the next lecture, I will talk about some exact relationships among numbers, that is, where the specific numbers definitely matter, and in Lectures Four and Five, Ed will show us the intrigue of counting exact numbers in nature and finding patterns among those numbers that then reflect back on nature.

Even in ancient times, numbers were viewed as fundamentally capturing the relationships and descriptions of our world. The Pythagorean Society in the sixth century B.C.E. had as its motto, "All is number," as they sought to describe everything from music to the heavens in terms of numerical relationships.

Of course, mathematics is not only about numbers. Mathematics really encompasses huge collections of ideas far beyond just numbers, and we will see examples of these and other ideas in future lectures. Nevertheless, the step of quantification will help us understand every aspect of mathematics and the world. When we look at geometrical structures, we will find that counting and quantifying our observations leads us to appreciate them more clearly. When we turn to probability, we will see that putting a numerical value on uncertainty allows us to put some order even on randomness.

In all cases, we are seeing the power of analyzing the world with more specificity by including quantitative reasoning among our habits of inquiry. I look forward to presenting the next lecture on "Fermat's Last Theorem and the Allure of Number."

Thank you.

Lecture Three
Fermat's Last Theorem and the Allure of Number

Michael Starbird, Ph.D.

Scope:

The natural numbers, besides their utility in counting, have captured the imaginations of people from different cultures around the world throughout history. The study of these natural numbers began several thousand years ago and continues with increasing vigor to this day. Mathematicians who are intrigued by numbers come to know them individually. To the eye of the mathematician, individual numbers have their own personalities—unique characteristics and distinctions that differentiate each number from the others. Here, we tell the true story of two giants of number theory who thrived in the early decades of the 20th century—Ramanujan and Hardy. This romantic story forms part of the mythology of mathematics. This lecture includes some insight into how numbers have been used and understood throughout the ages and closes with an ironclad proof that *every* natural number is, indeed, interesting.

Outline

I.   This lecture discusses one of the questions that stumped mathematicians for hundreds of years and spans ancient Babylonian times up to the present—the mystery of Fermat's last theorem.

   A. In 1637, in France, Pierre de Fermat was perusing a Greek mathematical text. As he was reading about Pythagorean triples, he wrote the following notation in the margin:

   > It is impossible to write a cube as a sum of two cubes, a fourth power as a sum of two fourth powers, and, in general, any power beyond the second as a sum of two similar powers. For this, I have discovered a truly wondrous proof, but the margin is too small to contain it.

   B. This assertion inspired thousands of hours of mathematical work over the next 350 years.

   C. In modern notation, Fermat's last theorem states that we cannot find natural numbers x, y, and z such that $x^n + y^n = z^n$, except when $n = 2$.

D. Fermat was probably reading about *Pythagorean triples*, such numbers as 3, 4, and 5 that have the property $3^2 + 4^2 = 5^2$.

E. Fermat made this assertion in 1637, and it was proved by Andrew Wiles in 1994. Fermat himself probably did not have the proof of his own theorem.

F. Fermat's theorem has no practical applications, but his story inspires us to believe that longstanding, complex problems can be solved.

II. Fermat's theorem goes back even earlier than the 17th century to ancient Babylonia.

   A. Archaeologists have found Babylonian tablets, dating from 1600 B.C.E. or earlier, showing two of the three numbers in Pythagorean triples. Again, these are sets of numbers that have the property $x^2 + y^2 = z^2$.

   B. Babylonians must have had some method for generating these numbers; they could not have been generated by chance. In ancient Greek times, we know that methods existed to generate Pythagorean triples.

   C. Let's learn how we can produce these Pythagorean triples, which are, of course, used to build right triangles.

      1. If we take any two natural numbers s and t, then $2st$, $s^2 - t^2$, and $s^2 + t^2$ form a Pythagorean triple.

      2. Writing these numbers out algebraically verifies that they create a Pythagorean triple: $(2st)^2 + (s^2 - t^2)^2 = (s^2 + t^2)^2$ because $4s^2t^2 + s^4 - 2s^2t^2 + t^4 = s^4 + 2s^2 2t^2 + t^4$.

      3. Let's choose some numbers for s and t and generate some Pythagorean triples. If we choose $s = 2$ and $t = 1$, we get the familiar 3, 4, 5. If we choose $s = 3$ and $t = 2$, we get 5, 12, and 13. If we choose $s = 7$ and $t = 4$, we get a result that is not familiar but is true, namely 56, 33, and 65.

      4. If we choose $s = 125$ and $t = 154$, we get the largest triples that appeared on the Babylonian tablet: 12709, 13500, and 18541.

III. Mathematics is not magic. It is developed by following the logical consequences of an idea. Let's trace this process for the generation of Pythagorean triples.

   A. Suppose we have a Pythagorean triple, that is, we have three numbers, a, b, and c, such that $a^2 + b^2 = c^2$. Let's further suppose that there is no common factor. We can argue, then, that one of a or b must be an odd number and one must be an even number.

   B. If we do a little algebra, bringing the b^2 to the other side of the equation, we are left with $a^2 = c^2 - b^2$.

   C. You may remember that the difference of two squares can be factored into $(c - b)(c + b)$.

   D. If a is an even number, it can be written as $2d$.

   E. Our equation at this point is: $4d^2 = (c - b)(c + b)$. Solving, we can see that we have a square that is equal to the product of two numbers.

   F. Because those two numbers have no common factor, we conclude that each of those two is a square, one of which we call s^2 and one of which we call t^2.

   G. The point of following this chain is to show that the s and t don't just come out of the blue; they are the product of algebraic thinking.

IV. What made Fermat believe that he could prove that no numbers could exist for $x^n + y^n = z^n$ when $n > 2$? He did prove the theorem for $n = 4$, and perhaps, his wonderful *method of descent* was at the heart of how he thought that all exponents could be proved.

   A. Sometimes it is easier to prove a hard theorem. We are trying to prove that the sum of two fourth powers cannot equal a fourth power; however, it is easier to prove that the sum of two fourth powers cannot even equal a perfect square. That is, we will prove that there do not exist non-zero integers, x, y, and z, so that $x^4 + y^4 = z^2$.

B. The method is to suppose we could find three numbers, x, y, and z, such that $x^4 + y^4 = z^2$.

C. From this equation, we use our knowledge of Pythagorean triples to deduce through several steps that if there were integers, x, y, and z, such that $x^4 + y^4 = z^2$, then there would be smaller natural numbers that satisfied that same condition.

D. Fermat's method of descent observes that this descent cannot go on forever; ultimately, we will reach one. Thus, there could not have existed numbers that meet the original condition.

E. The logic of that argument lies at the heart of the concept of natural numbers, that is, the fact that we start at 1 and that for each natural number, there is a next one. This means that we cannot have an infinitely long decreasing sequence of natural numbers.

V. The story of Fermat is an exploration of numbers for their own sake. Let's look at another category of numbers that is interesting for its own sake, *perfect numbers.*

A. A perfect number is a natural number that is equal to the sum of all its factors other than itself.

B. For example, 6 is a perfect number because 1+2+3 = 6. Another such number is 28 because 1+2+4+7+14 = 28.

C. The largest known perfect number is $2^{13466916}(2^{13466917-1})$. This perfect number was discovered in December 2001 and is the 39th perfect number known. It contains more than 8 million digits. If you wrote it out in small type, it would require more than 2000 pages.

D. No one knows whether there are infinitely many perfect numbers or whether there is an odd perfect number. Many interesting questions about numbers are unsolved to this day.

VI. Let's now turn to the story of Ramanujan, a self-trained mathematical genius from India in the early 1900s. His story celebrates the universality and universal appeal of numbers.

  A. Ramanujan independently discovered many formulas, including many that had stumped the greatest mathematicians from the Western world.

  B. In 1913, he wrote a letter to G.H. Hardy, a famous mathematician of the day, outlining some of his results.

  C. Hardy saw that Ramanujan was a true genius and brought him to England; the two men collaborated there for many years.

  D. When Ramanujan was in the hospital at one point, Hardy visited him and remarked that the number of his cab, 1729, was not very interesting. Ramanujan, who found all numbers interesting, replied, "On the contrary, 1729 is the smallest number that can be written as the sum of two cubes in two different ways."

VII. We end this lecture with an ironclad proof of the theorem that states that every natural number is interesting.

  A. We use Fermat's method of descent.

  B. Suppose there was any natural number that is not interesting. Is there any smaller natural number that is not interesting? Is there any smaller natural number than the second number chosen that is not interesting?

  C. Ultimately, we will arrive at the smallest natural number that is not interesting—and isn't that interesting?

Suggested Reading:

Edward B. Burger and Michael Starbird, *The Heart of Mathematics: An invitation to effective thinking*, Key College Publishing, Sections 2.1, "Counting: How the Pigeonhole principle leads to precision through estimation" and 2.3, "Prime Cuts of Numbers: How the prime numbers are the building blocks of all natural numbers."

Questions to Consider:

1. Write several Pythagorean triples of integers and for each triple use a meter stick to verify that the lengths form the sides of a right triangle.

2. Here is a game to be played with natural numbers. You start with any number. If the number is even, then you divide it by 2. If the number is odd, you triple it (multiply it by 3) and then add 1. Now you repeat the process with this new number. Keep going. You win (and stop) if you get to 1. Here is an example. If we start with 17 then we would have:

17, 52, 26, 13, 40, 20, 10, 5, 16, 8, 4, 2, 1—we see a 1, so we win!

Play this game with the starting numbers 19, 11, 22, and 30. Do you think you will always win no matter what number you start with? Here is one of many simple questions about numbers whose answer is unknown. No one knows the answer!

Lecture Three—Transcript
Fermat's Last Theorem and the Allure of Number

In the last lecture, we talked about the natural numbers; the numbers one, two, three, four, five, and so on, forever. And last time, we were talking about the natural numbers as if they were used for the purpose they were invented for, namely, counting things. We saw how they applied to counting numbers of people, and money, and all sorts of things.

For thousands of years, though, people have been curious about numbers for their own sake. In fact, one of the strategies of thinking that mathematics is really a paragon of is the strategy of abstracting from an idea, and then dealing with that abstract idea, and investigating it for its own sake. The natural numbers have been a collection of ideas that have inspired the imaginations of people from cultures around the world and throughout time, at least for thousands of years, people who have been investigating numbers for their own sake.

In this lecture, then, we're going to talk about one of the questions that stumped mathematicians for hundreds of years, and really ties us back to ancient Babylonian times, up to the modern day, so I thought you would enjoy hearing a little bit about Fermat's last theorem.

This story starts in 1637, in France, when Pierre de Fermat was sitting and reading a book, an ancient Greek mathematicians' book called *Arithmetica*. It was a book by Diophantus, and it was about numbers, talking about the relationships of numbers. As Fermat read this book, he looked at this book, and it was talking about *Pythagorean triples*, which I will tell you about in a little while.

He was reading this book, and he was taking notes, and in the margin of the book, he wrote the following little inscription that inspired tens of thousands of hours of work by mathematicians for the next 350 years. This is what he wrote. He said, "It is impossible to write a cube as the sum of two cubes, a fourth power as the sum of two fourth powers, and, in general, any power beyond the second as the sum of two similar powers. For this, I have discovered a truly wondrous proof, but the margin is too small to contain it." He wrote those words that, "the margin was too small to contain a proof of this statement," and then, 350 years passed without its being solved.

This is the statement as it would appear in modern-day notation. Here we see Fermat's last theorem. It would be expressed now by saying that you cannot find regular, whole numbers, x, y, and z, so that x, when raised to the n power (x^n), that is, x times x times x, n times, plus y to the n power, equals z to the n power ($x^n + y^n = z^n$). You cannot find non-zero numbers x, y, and z that satisfy that relationship, except for the exponent 2, ($n=2$).

You see, in this book that Fermat was reading, he was probably reading the section about *Pythagorean triples*. Those are numbers such as 3, 4, and 4. You see, 3, 3, and 5 have the property that three squared, that's nine, plus four squared, that's 16, equals 25, which equals five squared, $3^2 + 4^2 = 5^2$. Therefore, you see, Fermat's last theorem says that you cannot find a collection of three numbers like that if the exponent is bigger than two. However, we see that for the number two, there is such a number, and in fact, we will see that there are infinitely many numbers.

In 1637, then, Fermat posed this question, and it turns out that he was probably wrong in his assertion that he had a wondrous proof. He, by the way, didn't die until many years after writing this, so presumably, if he had had a proof, he would have made it known to somebody. However, he did prove related things, and we'll talk about some of those that he did prove. He wasn't able to prove his whole conjecture, though.

Three hundred and fifty seven years after he posed this question, in 1994, a gentleman by the name of Andrew Wiles, who is living today, proved that in fact Fermat was correct. However, we know for sure that Fermat did not have in mind the proof that Andrew Wiles constructed, because Andrew Wiles's proof is an enormously complicated thing. It involves mathematics that was developed in the 350 years since Fermat's time, ideas that Fermat never had, and that no one in his era had ever thought of. Mathematics is a developing subject. It's not all there, and it wasn't there in the 17th century; it is not there now. Things are being developed and discovered all the time. Whole ideas are being developed, and to attack this problem of Fermat's last theorem, the attack uses areas of geometry and other areas of mathematics that seem unrelated to a question about integers.

Andrew Wiles proved this theorem in 1994, after building on the work of many others. If Fermat had had that proof in mind, instead of writing "this margin is not large enough to contain it," a large truck would probably not have been large enough to contain the proof, because it took all of these thousands of pages of mathematics in the intervening years.

Fermat's theorem, first of all, has, in a sense, no practical application. Nobody is going to build a bridge using the fact that this is always true or not true, and in fact, at the time that it was proved— that is, that there were no integers x, y, and z, so that $x^n+y^n=z^n$—it was known to be true for all exponents up to hundreds of thousands. Thus, for all practical purposes, it was known to be true. There was no sense in which people were eagerly hanging on this question. On the other hand, though, the fact that it was unresolved for all these years has made it a real prize for mathematicians over the many, many centuries.

I think it also offers all of us a philosophical inspiration, namely, that here's an example of a problem that stumped all of humanity, and the best minds of the world were thinking about it for hundreds of years, and now, it is solved. Difficult, but it is solved. Maybe it gives us some hope, that problems of other sorts that have been unsolved for centuries or millennia can be solved. I think it has an inspirational value as well as a mathematical value.

I wanted to tie this Fermat's last theorem back even further than the 17th century, and go all the way back to ancient Babylonia. There's a Babylonian tablet that was written in the year 1600 B.C.E., or 1800, somewhere in that era, so that we're talking almost 4000 years ago, and on these tablets, there appear pairs of numbers. But actually, these pairs of numbers are two-thirds of triples of numbers. The triples of numbers are numbers with a property, like 3, 4, and 5, that one squared plus another one squared equals the third one squared (i.e., $3^2+4^2=5^2$). In ancient Babylonian times, then—and here you can see these examples that are numbers even into the thousands—where if you raise them to powers, you indeed see this relationship.

Well, when you see something like this, you know that the ancient Babylonians didn't have computers, for example. They could not do computer searches, and take five digit numbers and square them in order to find these numbers. There was probably some method that they used to find these numbers, but people don't really know whether they had a method. But it is known, though, in ancient Greek times, there were methods known to create these so-called

Pythagorean triples. So what we're going to do now is to talk about how it would be, if you wanted to create three numbers so that the square of the first plus the square of the second equals the square of the third, how you could do that. I will show how to construct infinitely many, as many as you want. You can just construct them all you want.

The neat thing about this—of course, the association you have with these numbers, $3^2+4^2=5^2$—is that you can build a right triangle because of the Pythagorean theorem. You know that the square of this side plus the square of this side is equal to the square of this side. You can build a right triangle that has integer length sides that is a perfect right triangle, and in fact, carpenters can use that to make a right triangle. You just take something that is three long and four long and five long, and stretch out, and you will make a perfect right triangle. The Pythagorean triples, then, can be generated by the following method. Here, I am going to show you how to do this.

You are seeking three numbers that have this property of the first squared plus the second squared equals the third squared, and in order to do that, you use two auxiliary numbers to create those three numbers. So what we'll do is we'll take two numbers and call them s and t. And if you take any integer s, any one you want, and any integer t, any other one you want, as long as they don't have any common factors, then, here's what you can do. You can take those two numbers, and create three numbers. One: two times the product of those two numbers, $2st$; the other: the square of the first minus the square of the second, s^2-t^2; the third one: the square of the first plus the square of the second, s^2+t^2. And you will create three numbers, and those three numbers will satisfy the condition that the first one squared plus the second one squared equals the third one squared, $(2st)^2+(s^2-t^2)^2=(s^2+t^2)^2$.

Now, there's just a little bit of algebra. Don't worry about it if you don't like the algebra, but it's very simple to see. The algebra is there on your screen. You can just see that if you take two numbers, s and t, any two numbers, if you take $2st$ and you square it, and you add it to $(s^2-t^2)^2$, when you expand that square, $(s^2-t^2)^2$ becomes $s^4-2s^2t^2+t^4$; when you add to that the $4s^2t^2$, which was $(2st)^2$, you can see that what you get is the expansion of $(s^2+t^2)^2$. Just this simple algebra, then, shows you that if you take any two numbers s and t, you can create this neat Pythagorean triple, or right triangle that has these properties.

Let's just do it for some simple ones and you'll see. Suppose you take $s=2$ and $t=1$. Let's just do the arithmetic; 2 (that's s) squared minus 1 (that's t) squared equals 3, $(2^2-1^2=3)$; 2 times the product of s and t, 2 times 2 times 1, is 4; then the final number is going to be the square of the first; that's 2^2, plus 1^2, that's 4 plus 1 is 5, and sure enough, we see that it is true that the first number generated, 3^2 plus 4^2 is equal to 5^2.

Let's do another one just for fun. You can just pick any two numbers you want, so this is something you can do in the privacy of your own home, you see? You can pick any two numbers, put them in there, and you get these Pythagorean triples, and you can actually build triangles that have integer sides, just by doing this. Let's try another one: $s=3$ and $t=2$. If we just do the arithmetic, once again: 3^2 minus 2^2, that's 9 minus 4 is 5; 2 times 3 times 2 is 12; and 3^2, that's 9, plus 2^2, that's 4 more, is a total of 13; and indeed, 5^2 plus 12^2 is equal to 13^2.

Those are familiar ones. Let's try one that's probably less familiar to you. We'll take two numbers at random: $s=7$ and $t=4$, and just doing the arithmetic again, taking the difference of their squares, we get 33. Their product times 2, we get 56, and the sum of their squares is 65. Indeed, if you take out your calculator, and you take 33 and square it, take 56 and square it, it equals 65^2.

I think these are sort of amazing, that you can create these triples by themselves. Well, let's think about the Pythagorean triples, and particularly, those big ones. You see, now maybe the Pythagoreans had a method, and by the way, there are different methods for creating all of these numbers, although this is the method that creates all of them. There are some other methods that would just create some of the Pythagorean triples. Just for fun, let's just note that if you choose s to be 125, and t to be 54, that those are the two numbers that create the Babylonians' Pythagorean triples that occurred on that clay tablet, the biggest ones that occurred on that clay tablet, and in fact, every one of the triples that appeared on that Babylonian tablet, and every other triple, can be created by choosing an s and a t appropriately.

I don't want people to feel that mathematics is a magical thing. When you see relationships like this, choosing s and t, and you square one and square the other, and you add them together, sometimes people think that mathematics just comes out of nowhere, or that some great genius just happened to think of it, and lives in a different world. That's really not the case, though. What actually happens with the way mathematics is developed is that people just have clear insight that is pushed forward in a logical, reasoned way, and that they get the insight by following logical consequences of good ideas.

Let's just see how you would guess to choose this number s and this number t, and create this combination of $(s^2+t^2)^2=(s^2-t^2)^2+(2st)^2$. How would you do that? The answer is this: Suppose you do the following analysis. Suppose you start with a Pythagorean triple; $a^2+b^2=c^2$. Suppose we have that triple, $a^2+b^2=c^2$. We can argue that either a or b has to be an odd number, and the other has to be an even number. It requires a tiny bit of work to figure out why that is the case, if a, b, and c don't have any common factors. If they had a common factor, we could divide it through, and get a simpler form. Let's just assume they don't have any common factor. Then, you can show that a is even, and b is odd, and c is odd.

Just doing a little bit of algebra, bringing the b^2 to the other side, we have the equation that $a^2=c^2-b^2$. Those of you who remember your algebra from high school, though, know that the difference of two squares can be factored into $(c-b)(c+b)$. Right? Additionally, if a is an even number, it can be written as 2 times some other number d, (i.e. $a=2d$ and therefore $a^2=4d^2$). We then have the little equation that $4d^2=(c-b)(c+b)$, and dividing by 4, and putting the 2 in each side, we can see that we have a square that is equal to the product of two numbers. These two numbers have no common factor, and so we conclude that each of those two is a square. We call one s^2 and the other one t^2, and that's where the s and the t come from.

Now, don't worry if you didn't follow the details of that. I actually didn't say all of the details of that. The point is, though, that just by doing a little bit of algebra, that's where those s and t's came from. They weren't just coming out of the blue.

What I am most interested in doing and in talking about, though, in this, is to go back to Fermat and his story. You see, Fermat wrote in that marginal note that you can't have such an equation, $x^n+y^n=z^n$, if n is bigger than 2. He actually was able to prove this for the case $n=4$. The proof that he developed for the case $n=4$—in other words, he proved that you cannot find numbers x, y, z, so that $x^4+y^4=z^4$, and he did conclusively prove that—and perhaps, he thought that that proof was so strong that it could be generalized to all the other exponents; I don't know, but that may have been the reason that he thought he could do more when he wrote that marginal note.

His method, though, develops a really intriguing strategy that is applied in mathematics in many settings, and it uses a fundamental property of the natural numbers. Here is his strategy. The goal is to prove that the sum of two fourth powers cannot equal a fourth power. But, it turns out to be easier to prove a harder theorem, namely that the sum of two fourth powers can't even equal a square. This is the way the proof goes. The strategy of the proof is suppose that you can find three numbers x, y, and z, so that $x^4+y^4=z^2$. Then, what we're going to do is do some analysis and conclude at the very end that if there were numbers x, y, and z that satisfy that condition, then there are smaller numbers also satisfy that condition. That's the strategy of the proof.

Here's the way that we do it. We use our knowledge of Pythagorean triples: x^4 remember is $(x^2)^2$; y^4 is $(y^2)^2$. So we have a Pythagorean triple $(x^2)^2+(y^2)^2=z^2$. Knowing what we do about Pythagorean triples, we know that those numbers, x, y, and z, are generated by s and t. So $x^2=2st$; $y^2=s^2-t^2$; and $z^2=s^2+t^2$. That means just doing a little algebra that $s^2=y^2+t^2$, which is just another Pythagorean triple. So whenever we see a Pythagorean triple, we know there are generating numbers that create those numbers. So we can find u and v, so that $s=u^2+v^2$; $y=u^2-v^2$; and $t=2uv$. When we substitute this last equation into the $x^2=2st$, or $x^2=2s(2uv)$, we get that $x^2=4suv$. This is one of the few times that a sports utility vehicle plays a crucial role in a mathematical proof.

Knowing that a perfect square, $x^2=4suv$, and s, u, and v, have no common factors, assuming that the original numbers didn't, we can substitute in and see that $s=e^2$, it's a perfect square so let's call that number e, u is a perfect square, so $u=f^2$; and $v=g^2$. So when we substitute into the formula $s=u^2+v^2$, we get that $e^2=(f^2)^2+(g^2)^2$ or $e^2=f^4+g^4$. So we have shown that the existence of the original equation gives us three more numbers where the numbers are smaller than the original ones.

Now, let's think about the logic of this, because this method, which is called Fermat's method of descent, is the crux of his whole proof, and is used many, many times in proofs in number theory. Namely, he proved the following: If you could find three numbers x, y, and z that satisfied this condition, then you could actually find three other numbers that satisfied the condition, but were smaller. Well, look, if you have three numbers that are smaller, and satisfy the condition— these are natural numbers, whole numbers, positive numbers—then you can find three others that are yet smaller. Then, you can find three others yet smaller than that. This can't go on forever, though. No matter how big the original numbers were, after a certain number of steps, a finite number of steps, you would get down to one. Then, you would have no place lower to go. You see? This actually proves that you cannot find numbers to begin with, because the fact that you could always find smaller ones means that they can't exist to begin with. This is a concept of Fermat's method of descent.

This is a story of the expiration of numbers that span from ancient Babylonian times to modern times, and it's interesting in that it is example of the expiration of numbers for their own sake, and I wanted to just give you a couple of other categories of numbers that people have investigated, that they found interest in, besides these squares and sums of squares. Others that are interesting are called *perfect numbers*. The ancient Greeks thought that a number was perfect, if you took its factors, if they added up, the factors less than it, and they added up to the number itself. For example, the number 6 is equal to the sum of its factors. 1 divides evenly into 6, so 1 plus 2 plus 3 is equal to 6.

Another perfect number is 28; 28 is equal to the sum of its factors: 1 plus 2 plus 4 plus 7 plus 14 is 28. People have been looking at these perfect numbers all through history, from ancient Greek times until now, and one discovered in the year 2001 is written there on your screen. It is 2 to the power of 13,466,916 times 2 to the power of one bigger than that minus 1 $[2^{13466916}(2^{13466917-1})]$. If you wrote that number out, it would have eight million digits. You could write it in some volumes. It would take more than 2000 pages of small type, to type that number, but that number has the property. That number, with eight million digits, has the property that, in fact, if you took all of its divisors, all the numbers less than it that divided evenly into it, and you added them up, you would get this number back again. Now there's a sort of amazing thing.

What really is interesting about the perfect numbers is not so much the ones that we know, or the fact that there are many we don't know, or whether there are infinitely many of them (this is the 39th one), but nobody knows whether there are any bigger than that and whether there are infinitely many bigger than that, or not. Additionally, nobody knows whether there are any odd perfect numbers. Nobody knows. This is an interesting fact about numbers, that most questions we consider about numbers are actually unsolved to this day.

I wanted to tell you about an individual mathematician whose love of numbers was particularly poignant, and plays a role in the history of mathematics in a special way. There was a mathematician from India in the early part of the 1900s. He was a self-trained mathematician, meaning that, in India at that time, they were not at the forefront of mathematical research. This mathematician did have some books, and there was a particular book that he had that had a lot of theorem statements without proofs, and he would go through and try to understand why they were true. This gentleman, whose name was Ramanujan, was a native genius of mathematics, and so even though he came from across the world and was not trained in a formal mathematical setting, the insights that he had into numbers, in particular, natural numbers—these whole, positive numbers—was so deep that he would write down these amazingly elaborate equations for relationships among numbers.

He wrote them down, and wrote a letter in 1913 to G.H. Hardy, who was one of the famous mathematicians of that era, and in that letter, he wrote a lot of his results. Some of the results were well known to Hardy. There were things that any beginning mathematician would know in that era. However, some of them were completely strange. Some of them were the kinds of things, where the questions that Western mathematical tradition was asking were not even the questions he was answering, so that they weren't even answering the right questions, so to speak. They were asking different questions. The thing that Ramanujan thought was interesting, some of them were different from those that the Western mathematical tradition was asking.

Others that Ramanujan had insight into were ones that had puzzled Western mathematicians for a long time, and that he was able to penetrate and solve. It was clear to G.H. Hardy that Ramanujan was a true genius, and Hardy brought Ramanujan over to England, and they collaborated for years in a very fruitful collaboration between the two of them. Ramanujan was not used to the weather in England, though. It was very cold, and he didn't like the food, so he got sick, and one of stories of this is that he was in the hospital at one time in England, and Hardy came to the hospital to visit Ramanujan.

Hardy came in, and for those of you who may or may not know mathematicians, mathematicians are not necessarily the most human sorts, you know, the most glib and easy-speaking people in the world. This was probably the case with these two. Hardy sat there, and purportedly, this was the conversation. He said, "Well, the cab I arrived in was Number 1729. It doesn't seem very interesting to me." To which Ramanujan replied, "Oh, on the contrary, my dear Hardy, 1729 is the smallest number that can be written as the sum of two cubes in two different ways." Thus, Ramanujan was a person who really knew his numbers intimately. Well, so this was a story where, when people get to love numbers, they can really see a difference in them.

I wanted to end with a proof of the following theorem: That every natural number is interesting. This is an ironclad proof you all have to believe, so here's the thing. Suppose there were any natural number that was not interesting. We're going to use Fermat's method of descent. If that number were not interesting, is there any smaller number that's not interesting? If there is, take that. If there's a smaller one, take that, and so on. Keep going until you get to the smallest natural number that is not interesting. You see, if there were any uninteresting natural number, there would be a smallest uninteresting natural number. Look, though. If you have a number that is the smallest uninteresting number, isn't that interesting? That is an ironclad proof that you couldn't have started with a number that was uninteresting to begin with, and it uses exactly Fermat's method of descent to convince us of this fact about numbers.

Lecture Four
Pining for Nature's Numbers

Edward B. Burger, Ph.D.

Scope:

Often when we see beauty in nature, we are subconsciously sensing hidden order—order that itself has an independent richness and beauty. To illustrate this maxim, we stop to smell the roses or, more accurately, to count spirals among the florets of a coneflower. In the coneflower, the pinecone, and the pineapple, we find a number pattern called the *Fibonacci numbers*. This simple sequence of numbers has surprising structure that leads us not only to mathematical insights but also to issues of aesthetics. Fibonacci numbers touch such diverse fields as architecture and painting. We begin our investigation, however, firmly rooted in nature and uncover its incredible pattern and structure.

Outline

I. Examining the world around us opens surprising vistas. Looking deeply into nature, we see unexpected patterns with rich structure.

    A. The pineapple is covered with bumps that exhibit a surprising geometric structure.

        1. One way of seeing more in the world is to move from a qualitative description to a quantitative one.

        2. In the case of the pineapple, we can count the spirals.

        3. In a surprising twist, we discover that all (or most) pineapples have the same number of spirals—8 in one direction and 13 in the other.

    B. Moving to the coneflower, we see spirals among the florets inside the flower.

        1. As before, let's not be content with a qualitative impression; let's count the spirals.

        2. In one direction, the number of spirals is 13, the same as on the pineapple.

        3. In the other direction, the number of spirals is 21.

        4. So far, the collection of numbers we have is 8, 13, 21.

    C. If we look at a daisy, we also see spirals, 21 in one direction and 34 in the other.

D. The pinecone has 5 spirals in one direction and 8 in the other.

E. The numeric coincidences arising from our spiral counts prompt us to look for an underlying structure.
　　1. At this point, our collection of numbers is 5, 8, 13, 21, 34.
　　2. Each number in the sequence is the sum of the previous two numbers.
　　3. If we move out of nature into the abstract, how would the pattern continue? The next numbers would be 55, 89, 144….
　　4. Can we also go backwards in the pattern? The first numbers in the pattern must be 1, 1, 2, 3.

F. Somehow, nature reflects this simple pattern of 1, 1, 2, 3, 5, 8, 13, 21, 34….
　　1. In mathematics, when we make an abstract discovery, we often try to apply it to the real world.
　　2. In a sunflower, we see a much larger spiral. Following the pattern, we might guess that its number of spirals would be 55 and 89, and we would be correct.
　　3. The abstract world of mathematics allows us to gain a richer and more accurate understanding of the everyday world.

G. Neither mathematicians nor biologists completely understand why we see these numbers in the natural world.
　　1. One theory begins with the fact that the tiny florets that we are counting are each individual flowers, making up what is known as a *composite flower*.
　　2. Flowers grow up from the center. As each of the tiny yellow florets in the center of a daisy, for example, becomes part of the flower, it must move out of the way to make room for florets coming in behind it.
　　3. Assuming that each floret needs as much space as possible around it to grow, the result is the spirals that we see when we look closely at the flower.

II. The collection of numbers that we have been examining is called the *Fibonacci sequence*, named after a 13th-century mathematician, Leonardo of Pisa.

A. In 1202, Leonardo wrote a treatise on mathematics, posing what is now a famous question about the reproductive behavior of rabbits.

B. We start with a pair of baby rabbits. Starting at two months, they produce one pair of baby rabbits each month from then on. Each baby pair follows the same pattern. How many pairs of rabbits will we have at the end of a year?

C. If we illustrate the question for the first four months, we see that the number of rabbits follows the Fibonacci sequence.

D. Can we explain this amazing occurrence of the pattern?
  1. At month 3, we have two pairs of adult rabbits and one baby pair. How many additional pairs will be added in month 4?
  2. We can see that we add the numbers of rabbits in months 2 and 3 to find the number for month 4. All the rabbits from month 2 will be adults by month 3 and will be able to procreate in month 4.

E. At the end of a year, there will be 233 pairs of rabbits.

III. Can the natural numbers themselves be generated by the Fibonacci numbers?

  A. Obviously, not all the natural numbers are in the Fibonacci sequence, but we do have a method to allow the Fibonacci numbers to produce any natural number.

  B. As an example, let's use 45, which is not a Fibonacci number. Can we use the Fibonacci numbers to produce 45?

  C. The largest Fibonacci number that is smaller than 45 is 34. We would need to add 11 to 34 to get 45, but 11 is not a Fibonacci number either.

  D. The number 11 is also smaller than 45, so let's repeat the process: 11 falls between the Fibonacci numbers 8 and 13, and we can write 11 as 8+3, the sum of two Fibonacci numbers.

  E. We can write 45, then, as 34+8+3. Indeed, every natural number can be expressed as the sum of Fibonacci numbers.

  F. This decomposition of natural numbers is called the *Zeckendorff decomposition*, after the mathematician who first noticed it in the 20th century.

IV. If we look at the Fibonacci numbers themselves, we notice that only two principles are at play.

   A. All we have to know to generate the sequence are the first two numbers—1, 1—and the process.

   B. This sequence is an example of a *recurrence sequence*. We use the previous numbers to generate the next numbers.

   C. If we use different starting numbers but the same process, we will generate a different sequence. Suppose we start with 2 and 1. The resulting sequence would be: 2, 1, 3, 4, 7, 11, 18, 29, 47, 76, 123….

   D. This is called the *Lucas sequence*, named after a 19th-century French mathematician.

   E. The Lucas sequence seems to have very little in common with the Fibonacci numbers. After the first three, none of the numbers in the Lucas sequence are Fibonacci numbers. Is there any relationship? We will explore this question in the next lecture.

   F. When we look for patterns and structure in our world, we will find them. An effective method of thinking is to look constantly for patterns to bring the world into sharper focus.

Suggested Reading:

Edward B. Burger and Michael Starbird, *The Heart of Mathematics: An invitation to effective thinking*, Key College Publishing, Section 2.2, "Numerical Patterns in Nature: Discovering nature's beauty and the Fibonacci numbers."

Questions to Consider:

1. Let F_n denote the nth Fibonacci number. By experimenting with numerous examples in search of a pattern, determine a formula for $(F_{(n+1)})^2 + (F_n)^2$, that is, a formula for the sum of the squares of two consecutive Fibonacci numbers.

2. Suppose we start with one pair of baby rabbits, and again they create a new pair every month, but this time, let's suppose that it takes two months before a pair of bunnies is mature enough to reproduce. Make a table for the first 10 months indicating how many pairs there would be at the end of each month. Do you see

a pattern? Describe a general formula for generating the sequence of rabbit pair counts.

Lecture Four—Transcript
Pining for Nature's Numbers

In the past two lectures, Mike has been sharing with us the idea, concept, and notion of numbers, and today, I want to continue that theme, and now, fold nature into the mix.

The 19th century philosopher Auguste Comte once wrote: "There is no inquiry which is not finally reducible to a question of Numbers; for there is none which may not be conceived of as consisting in the determination of quantities by each other, according to certain relations."

That really is the theme of today's lecture—looking for patterns and relations. And so often, not just in mathematics but in life, if we seek patterns, all of a sudden we find them. And once we find them, structure emerges, and all of a sudden things that up to this point appeared invisible, come into focus.

I want to illustrate that by looking at a very, very special collection of numbers—and this is a collection of numbers that in fact is all around us all the time—where would you possibly see this? Well, let's start at the grocery store. If you were to take a look at a pineapple, well, it's kind of an attractive pineapple; it's actually nice and ripe. It smells good; we will probably be enjoying this in a little bit. If you look closely at a pineapple, though, you actually see that there's lots of structure here, and with very close inspection, if you look at things really, really carefully, you'll see that on the face of the pineapple, we actually see spirals. You can see them, and these spirals appear—one starts right here and goes up to here; there's another one that goes right underneath it, and another one underneath it, and we see these spirals beginning to emerge.

Once you see structure, if you look closely, you can see even more. In this case, if you look really closely, in fact, you'll see that there are spirals even going the other direction, so that we have these clockwise spirals that seem to also run in parallel, and then the spirals and these spirals mesh together to make the beautiful façade of the pineapple.

Well, as Mike was advertising in the previous lectures, when we have quantities, so often in life, it's great just to count them. In fact, let's actually count the spirals and see how many we have. This is like one of those cooking shows. I've actually done it in advance. Here's the pineapple. And if we want to count the spirals, one way to count them is to mark them. So here, you can see that this has already been marked, and you can see that the spirals are very clearly marked in red except for this one here. This one is in gold, and you may say, "Gee, Ed, did you run out of the red?" The truth is, I did this on purpose, and you can probably guess why; that way, I know where I start. One time, I was counting spirals, and I did it for days before I realized that I had already done it.

We will start the gold, and we will just count the number of spirals. Here we go. Starting on the gold, we have 1, 2, 3, 4, 5, 6, 7, 8 and now I have returned back. I have eight spirals going this way. Now let's count how many spirals we have going the other way. Let's take a look at that. I've actually worked that out in advance as well. Here we are. Maybe it's the same number. Let's take a look and see, and count. I will start counting here, again, on the gold. I have 1, 2, 3, 4, 5, 6, 7, 8, 9, 10, 11, 12, 13. I have eight going in one direction, and 13 going in the other.

Well, that is sort of peculiar. Maybe we would have thought there were the same number of spirals, but somehow, maybe a pineapple can tell right-handedness from left-handedness; I don't know.

Well, in fact, spirals abound in nature. If we take a look, for example, at the coneflower, we see many, many spirals, and that is what we are looking at right now as an example, a picture of a coneflower. Let's actually count these spirals. We'll do it right now, together. If we count in one direction, what we see is 1, 2, 3, 4, 5, 6, 7, 8, 9, 10, 11, 12, 13. Well, that's an amazing coincidence. Notice that one of the spiral counts on the coneflower is exactly the same as one of the spiral counts on the pineapple, so that is sort of an amazing coincidence. Let's now count the spirals the other way, so here we go; I'm going to count the spirals the other way, and let's see how many there are. I'll count now again: 1, 2, 3, 4, 5, 6, 7, 8, 9, 10, 11, 12, 13, 14, 15, 16, 17, 18, 19, 20, 21.

We see that there are 21 spirals in the other direction. What's our collection of numbers, our number sequence so far? Well, we saw eight. Then we saw 13, and the next number we saw was twenty-one. Now, in fact, if you look at a beautiful daisy, the yellow portion of a daisy, again, you will see spirals. Suddenly, the world opens up once you look at it very, very closely, which is a great, great life lesson. If you were to count the spirals on a daisy—I will assign that as a homework—you would actually see, in one direction, 21, again, an amazing coincidence that agrees with one of the previous counts, one of the spiral counts for the coneflower, and then, in the other direction, it's actually bigger, we get thirty-four.

Right now, then, our list of numbers consists of 8, 13, 21, and 34. It turns out that you can find spirals in all sorts of things. For example, right here, on this little side table sits a pinecone. Pinecones you can find anywhere in the forest. And again, now you can start to see those spirals emerging here, and also emerging here, and if you count the spirals on a pinecone—sort of a modest pinecone—you're going to see five and eight, and remember, actually, eight was the smaller spiral count of the pineapple.

Lots of coincidences, so many coincidences that we have to wonder whether there might be some hidden structure. Let's look at this nice sequence of numbers that we've collected. It's 5, 8, 13, 21, 34. Now, when you look at that collection of numbers, all of a sudden, we see an amazing pattern, an incredible pattern.

Notice what happens if you take the first two numbers, 5 and 8, and just add them up. We get the next number on the list, 13. Now take 8 and 13 and add those numbers up. What are we left with? Twenty-one. What if we take 13 and 21, and add them? What do we get? We get 34.

All of these different spiral counts that came from different fruit and flora, and so forth, turn out to have an incredible structure when they are taken as a whole. Now, why in the world are we finding this structure?

Well, first of all, let's see that we can actually continue this pattern. Let's go from nature to the abstract world of mathematics. For example, if we were to continue the process, what would be the next number? The next number on this list, if we were just to continue the pattern, would be what? We would take the 21 and 34, and add them, and we would get 55. What would be the next number? We would take the 34 and the 55, and add them up, and get 89. The next number would be 144. The next number would be 233.

Once we see the pattern, we can sort of move forward. In fact, we could even go backward in the pattern. In particular, what would be the number that would have to come right before the 5? Well, let's think about it. It has to be a number so that when I add it to 5, I get 8. That means that it must be 3. What is the number that must come before that? Well, it's a number that I add to 3 in order to make the 5. That would be 2. What would come before that? Well, it's a number that I have to add to 2 in order to make it equal to 3, and that is 1. What's the one that comes before that? It is the number that I have to add to 1 to make it 2, which would be 1, so that I could even work backwards

Now we have this long list of numbers, or a number sequence, which goes 1, 1, 2, 3, 5, 8, 13, 21, 34, 55, 89, and it just keeps going, and going, and going. The pattern continues. You just keep taking two numbers and adding them, and you get the next one.

Now, what we are seeing, though, is that somehow nature is reflecting this amazingly simple pattern. Well, this is the great thing about mathematics. When we make an abstract discovery, so often, we can take that abstract discovery and fold it back into our everyday world. Let's take a look at a picture of a sunflower. Now, there you see that huge, spiral, smiling face looking at you. Without counting at all, what might you guess those spiral counts to be? Well, if you now have that abstract pattern in front of you, when you see how the previous sequence of spirals fell into this pattern, you might guess that the next pair of counts might be 34 and 55, or maybe 55 and 89, and it turns out that you would be correct. It turns out that if you count the very large spirals in a sunflower, you will see either 34, 55—if it is a small one—or 55 and 89.

The abstract realm of mathematics, then, allows us to see and predict our own everyday world in a richer way, in a more accurate way. Suddenly, invisible structure, structure that was there all the time—we never noticed the connection—comes into focus.

Now that we see how mathematics can really allow us to understand our own world even better, through predicting what the spiral counts on the sunflower would be, this does sort of raise a biological question which I am not an expert at, which is: How come we see these spirals, for example, in the flowers, in the daisy, in the coneflower, and in the sunflower? Well, actually, this is a question that is not completely understood by mathematicians or biologists. There are some interesting theories, though, and I wanted to share one theory with you.

One theory asserts that the tiny florets, or those little teeny flower pieces that we were counting, those little teeny buds, in fact, are each, in fact, an individual flower. In fact, all of these flowers, it turns out, are examples of what are known as *composite flowers*. I didn't know this, by the way, but I was talking to a biology colleague, and she taught me all about this. It turns out that with the daisy, for example, every single one of those little yellow florets that we count, every single one of those little teeny things, as well as every single one of those white petals, by definition of "flower," is its own flower, and they all come together to make this, what's called a composite flower, so that this one flower actually has all of these little flowers inside of it.

Let's look at the yellow center, all the little, teeny flowers, those florets in there. It turns out that the way these flowers actually grow, when you are starting from the infancy of a flower, is that they start to grow from the very center, said that it goes up from the stalk, and blossoms out, and as the buds come out of the center, they have to move and expand to make room for the new buds that are coming out from the center, pushing them out. Everyone's being pushed out to the boundary as the younger little florets come into play.

Now, what if we make the hypothesis that these florets, these little, teeny yellow buds, are just like people? They want as much land around them as possible. They want a little plot of land, raise their families, have some acreage, you know, they might say, "We've got two-thirds of an acre." "Oh, good for you."

If you just assume then, that namely, these little florets are going to move themselves and position themselves in such a way that they have as much room around them as they possibly can, given the constraints of the flower, and constantly pump in new florets from the very, very center, and have them push out, and the older flowers get further and further out to the boundary, when you do this, and fill up all space, you get these spirals, and if you count the spirals, we see, in fact, we get the *Fibonacci numbers*.

If we assume that, in fact, these florets want as much space around them as possible as they grow, then that would explain why we have the spiral counts, so that this might actually explain why we see these numbers.

Well, that's an explanation that is a great theory, but these numbers themselves, in mathematics, are extremely interesting, and in fact, they are called the *Fibonacci numbers*, which maybe some of you have heard of. They are named after, in fact, the 13th-century mathematician Leonardo de Pisa. Now, Leonardo de Pisa, that was his name, also went by the name "Fibonacci," since, in fact, he was a member of the Bonacci family. That explains that, and actually, I want to tell you a little, cute piece of trivia that I happened to know, which is that Fibonacci himself actually had his own nickname as he referred to himself, which was "Bigallo." Now, *bigallo* be interpreted as either a much-traveled man, or a good-for-nothing. Well, it's well documented that he was extremely well-traveled, and it's also well documented that he was fascinated with mathematical questions that appeared to have no practical value, so that when he called himself "Bigallo," did he mean "well-traveled," or "good-for-nothing"? I will leave it to you to see what he meant.

Anyway, in the year 1202, he actually wrote a treatise on arithmetic and algebra, and it was entitled *Liber abaci*, and in it, he posed the now very, very famous question, and I want to read it to you: "A certain man put a pair of rabbits in a place surrounded all sides by a wall. How many pairs of rabbits can be produced from that pair in a year if it is supposed that every month each pair begets a new pair which from the second month on becomes productive?"

That was the question that he posed in the book, and I want us to think about it a little bit. First of all, it's sort of complicated; you have to wrap your mind around what this question even is. We start off with a pair of baby rabbits. Now, that pair of baby rabbits are babies, but a month later, they'll become adult rabbits, and from that point onward, they actually, as you know rabbits tend to do, tend to procreate. From that point on, every month, that pair of rabbits can produce another pair of rabbits as offspring, and then, this pattern continues.

Let's actually take a look at it, and I will see if I can act it out for you, but this will be a "G" rated version, I assure you. We start off with month one, with just a pair of bunnies, and they're fine. Now, a month later, they grow up, but they're too young, of course, to actually produce any offspring, so the next month, you see, they're just bigger. This is the same pair, but just bigger. Now, what happens the month that follows?

Now, these are adults, so they can actually produce little babies of their own, so that in fact, they're still around, so here's that same couple the second month, but now, they actually can procreate, and they produce little offspring. Isn't that cute? See, there're some little offspring.

Now, what happens in the next month? Well, these rabbits are still here, of course. This is taking place over a year, so remember, we are going to assume that none of the rabbits has an untimely demise. What happens to this little baby pair? Well, this baby pair, a month later, becomes adult, so in fact, they grow up. Here they are, all grown up. Of course, though, this adult pair, in the next month, continues to produce babies, so they actually produce another pair of offspring, so we also see a brand new pair of offspring, generated by this adult pair.

Now we're at this month, so what's going to happen the following month? Well, let's again look at the pattern. These adults are still going to remain, so we still have those adults. Here's the original adult pair, and then, we have this new additional adult pair, and what about these little bunnies? A month later, of course, they're all grown up, so that in fact, now we see that they have become adults. Now, how many new babies are there going to be?

Well, let's look back here. This is an adult pair, which will produce a pair of babies in the next month, so that we're going to have a pair from them, but now, this is an adult pair, and they are actually able to procreate now, and so, they're going to produce some babies. That's where we are after one, two, three, four months. That's where we are. The question is: How many would there be at the end of a year?

Well, let's just see if we can see a pattern. Let's just count how many pairs of rabbits there are at every stage. When we start, we have one, then I have one, that I have two pairs; then I have one, two, three pairs; then I have one, two, three, four, five pairs. Do you see the pattern? It's the *Fibonacci sequence* again. It's the Fibonacci sequence. Amazing. This is why the sequence is called the Fibonacci sequence.

Now, does this pattern continue? Can we explain it? Now that we see this amazing phenomenon, can we try to make it intuitive? The answer is "yes," just by thinking about the process. Let's, in fact, just explore what happens as we move from this case to this case. Let's return back to here. Here I have two adult pairs and a baby pair. Now, what's going to happen? We know that all three of these pairs are going to live on in the next month, so there they all are, and how many new additional pairs do we add? Well, as many as we had not here, but here, because we know at this stage, whatever rabbits we have will be adults by the time they get to here, and therefore, they will be able to procreate here.

What do we do? We take the number of pairs we have here, and we add to that the number of pairs we had before. I take the previous two months', and add them together to reveal how many we have at the next month. You can see the Fibonacci pattern, and it's interesting to notice that this is the first instance where these are called the Fibonacci numbers. This is where people start to realize this sequence was interesting. But of course, nature had us all beat, because of course, nature encoded this wonderful sequence in its spirals long before Fibonacci came along in the 13th century, so that it's sort of wonderful to see that after awhile, humankind can even catch up with nature in some things. But nature came first, so even though we called it the Fibonacci numbers, maybe we should be calling it "nature's numbers."

Here we see an example where the Fibonacci numbers can be used to emulate the reproductive habits of bunnies. By the way, what is the answer to the question? Maybe I should tell you, because you might be wondering, "After a year, what happens?" We have to keep repeating this, and so, it's going to be some Fibonacci number, and I will let you think about which one it is, but I'll tell you the answer. There are going to be 233 pairs of rabbits left at the end of the year, so there are going to be lots. I hope this enclosed area was quite large, because you're going to have lots of bunnies, and a lot of bunnies to feed, by the way, and to clean up after, so it could be bad.

That explains the Fibonacci tale, and that's wonderful. We see that, in fact, the Fibonacci numbers can be applied to describe the reproductive habits of bunnies, but in fact, maybe, the natural numbers themselves can be generated, and can be reproduced by the Fibonacci numbers. You see, if you actually look at the Fibonacci numbers, I guess one thing that you noticed after you discovered the amazing pattern is that not all the natural numbers are listed. Right? The numbers 1, 2, 3, 4, 5, 6, 7, 8, 9, 10, 11, and so forth. They are not all on that list. We only have some of them. It's sort of sad to realize, for example, that poor number four is not a Fibonacci number, and that is sort of sad, because the Fibonacci numbers get all this press, and here, poor, lonely number four is off on its own, so that we might be feeling badly for the other numbers.

Well, it turns out that there actually is a way to allow the Fibonacci numbers to produce any natural number, so that in fact, we can see the reproductive process even in the abstract setting of mathematics. Let me illustrate this with an actual example, so you can see this sort of happening live.

Let's take a number, for example, 45. Now, 45 is not a Fibonacci number, and you can tell that just by looking at the list of Fibonacci numbers, and you see 1, 1, 2, 3, 5, 8, 13, 21, 34, 55. We actually jumped over the number 45, so 45 is not a Fibonacci number. It's not a Fibonacci number.

Okay, well, that is sort of sad, but now, let's see if we can somehow use the Fibonacci numbers to produce 45. The natural guess might be to say, "Well, what is the biggest Fibonacci number that is smaller than it?" What is the one that sort of comes close? Well, it would be 34. Thirty-four is the largest Fibonacci number that in fact is smaller than 45. I could take 45, and say, "Okay, well, it's 34, a Fibonacci number. Great. Plus a little bit of error, and what do I have to add to 34 to make it 45?" Well, the answer is 11. What I can see is that I can write 45 as a Fibonacci number, 34+11, but sadly, if you think back to the Fibonacci numbers, 11 is not, alas, a Fibonacci number, so that is sort of sad.

We have actually made some progress, though, because 11 is a number that is smaller than 45. Why not repeat this process with the smaller number, 11? In particular, let's find the Fibonacci number that is as large as possible, but smaller than 11. Let's see where 11 fits in. Well, we have 1, 1, 2, 3, 5, 8, 13. Ah, so 11 fits in between 8 and 13. Let's take 11 and write it as 8 plus some little error. What's the error in this case? Well, 11, of course, equals 8+3. Oh, wait, but 3 is a Fibonacci number!

Look what we have just done. We have taken this unseemly non-Fibonacci number, 45, and we have written it as 34+8 +3, and so, what we see is that this number, 45, while it's not a Fibonacci number, can be expressed as the sum of Fibonacci numbers, and that's true with every single natural number that you can think of.

This process that we used will actually always work. No matter how big the number is, all you have to do is go backwards from that number until you hit the first Fibonacci number. Then, look at the difference between that number and the original number that you are looking at.

In particular, if you have some big number, you find the Fibonacci number that comes right before it, and you say, "What do I have to add to that Fibonacci number to make it equal to the number that we are looking at?" Well, that amount that you have to add is actually smaller than the original number, and so, it is a sort of a divide-and-conquer approach. We start with a big number, we rip off some Fibonacci number, and now, we're left with a smaller number, and now, we just repeat. So often in life, the idea of divide-and-conquer is a very powerful way to analyze, understand, and resolve really complicated issues. If you have a really, really big issue and it's too hard to comprehend it, just try to make it a little bit simpler. Make a little bit of progress, and then repeat the process, again, and again, and again, and again, and all of a sudden, you have this thing resolved, or in this case, you would have a collection of Fibonacci numbers that add to any natural number that you can think of.

By the way, this decomposition of any number into the sum of Fibonacci numbers is actually called the *Zeckendorf decomposition*, named after the mathematician Zeckendorf, who first noticed this in the 20th century.

Well, so, that's great, and we see this idea of divide-and-conquer, and that's wonderful, and so forth, but let's now look at the sequence of Fibonacci numbers in their own right, and notice something interesting about them; that really, there are only two things at play here. The two things at play here are the following: All we have to know are the first two numbers, the 1, 1. We can think of those as starting seeds. Then, the process, which is you take those two, and add them to get the next one. Then, you take the two previous ones, add those, and get the next one. That is sort of a generating process. Really, then, the Fibonacci numbers can be expressed very simply with just two pieces of fact, two starting seeds, and then the process of adding the two to get the next one, adding the previous two to get the next one, and so on and so forth.

In fact, this sequence is an example of what is called a *recurrence sequence*, because I used the previous numbers to generate the next numbers. All I need to know are the first two numbers and the process.

If you think that way, then we can even generalize the Fibonacci numbers, and look for even more exotic collections of numbers by doing what? By just starting with different starting seeds. For example, suppose we start with the starting seeds 2, 1, rather than 1, 1. If we start with 2, 1, but keep the same generating process, then what do we see? Well, 2 plus 1 would be 3, so the next number would be 3, and then we take 1 plus 3, which is 4, and then we take 3 plus 4, which is 7, and that we take 4 plus 7, which is 11, and if you keep repeating this, you would see that there would be a new sequence of numbers that would begin: 2, 1, 3, 4, 7, 11, 18, 29, 47, 76, and it keeps going, and going, and going.

Now, in fact, this sequence also has a name. This is called the *Lucas sequence*. A lot of people actually call it the Lucas sequence, but it really should be pronounced "Lucah," because it is actually named after the 19th-century mathematician Eduard Lucas, who was a French mathematician who was one of the mathematicians exploring the idea of recurrence sequences. It's really named in his honor.

Now, if you look at this recurrence sequence, you will notice that in fact, there's very little in common with the Fibonacci numbers. The first couple of numbers are the same, because I just picked 2, 1. But once the process gets going, you see numbers like 4, 7, 11, 18, 29, 47, and so on. You'll notice that none of them are the same, or equal to the Fibonacci numbers. These are two different lists after you get past the first couple of numbers. Here's a question: Can there be, potentially, any similarity between these two sequences of numbers?

Well, they certainly look completely different. They look completely different, yet they do share something in common. Namely, they do have the same generating property. However, we started with different starting seeds, so certainly, the numbers are going to be completely different, and potentially unrelated. Well, in the next lecture, we're actually going to explore this issue, and in particular, explore the Fibonacci numbers in their own right. Instead of considering nature as a means to discover the Fibonacci numbers, in the next lecture, we're going to look at the nature of Fibonacci numbers themselves, and we're going to discover some surprising and amazing coincidences between the Fibonacci numbers and this new list of numbers, the Lucas numbers.

The surprise here is that when we look for pattern and structure in our world, and in mathematics, we will find it, and so, a wonderful lesson for thinking is to constantly search for patterns, and all of a sudden, through that process, worlds that have been in front of us all this time suddenly come sharply into focus. It's as though we've been looking at the world in a sort of blurry fashion throughout our whole lives in this particular aspect, whatever that area is, but through careful thought, careful thinking, and looking for a pattern, we actually see that thing more sharply, and more in focus, and suddenly, the structure that was in front of us and that was never noticeable before, comes into focus.

In the next lecture, we will take a look at the nature of Fibonacci numbers themselves, and we will explore, and see beauty in a more abstract realm. From nature, we're off and running with the Fibonacci numbers.

Lecture Five
Sizing up the Fibonacci Numbers

Edward B. Burger, Ph.D.

Scope:

A potent method for discovering new insights is to isolate patterns from what we directly observe, then look at those patterns by themselves. In this lecture, we will move beyond the plant origins of the Fibonacci numbers and consider the Fibonacci sequence as an interesting entity in its own right. We conduct this investigation with the hope and expectation that interesting relationships that may arise among Fibonacci numbers may have reflections back in our world.

We observed that flowers, pinecones, and pineapples all display consecutive pairs of Fibonacci numbers. In each case, the number of spirals in one direction was not quite twice as great as the number of spirals in the other direction. By moving from an estimate ("not quite twice") to the precise, we find ourselves led inexorably from the numerical to the geometrical to discover the most pleasing proportion in art and architecture: the *Golden Mean*.

Outline

I. In this lecture, we move from the Fibonacci numbers in nature to the nature of the Fibonacci numbers themselves. We also see the importance of making mistakes and learning from our mistakes as strategies for thinking.

    A. How fast do Fibonacci numbers grow? Each subsequent one is not quite double its predecessor.

        1. For example, 3 is not quite the double of its predecessor, 2. We also note that the difference between the double of 2 (that is, 4) and 3 is 1.

        2. Again, 5 is not quite the double of 3, and the difference between that double (6) and 5 is 1.

        3. The difference between the double of 5 (10) and 8 is 2. As we move through the Fibonacci sequence, we see that the differences are also Fibonacci numbers.

    B. The sequence displays an interesting pattern, namely:

2 × the next Fibonacci number

– the Fibonacci number two before the last

the next Fibonacci number

We can use this formula to find the next Fibonacci number after 13: $2(13) - 5 = 21$.

C. Now let's consider a different way of looking at the relative sizes of Fibonacci numbers.

    1. In particular, we'll explore the quotients of consecutive Fibonacci numbers.

    2. If we begin dividing one Fibonacci number by the previous one and constructing a list of the quotients, we see that the results all seem to hone in on a particular number: 1.618033989....

D. Let's take a look at a puzzle paradox that may lead us to a more dramatic realization of this observation.

    1. We start with a square that is 8 units by 8 units. Its area, of course, is 64.

    2. The same puzzle pieces that formed the square can be rearranged to make a 13 × 5 rectangle. Its area is 65.

    3. Where did the extra unit of area come from? If we arrange the pieces so that the corners just meet for the rectangle, we see a region in the middle that is not closed; that region has 1 unit of area.

E. This puzzle allows us to devise a formula that relates to the quotients of Fibonacci numbers.

    1. If we take three consecutive Fibonacci numbers, such as 5, 8, and 13, and we square the middle number, the result will be off by 1 from the product of the flanking numbers.

    2. The formula is:.

$$\frac{\text{middle Fibonacci \#}}{\text{first Fibonacci \#}} - \frac{\text{last Fibonacci \#}}{\text{middle Fibonacci \#}} = \pm \frac{1}{(\text{first Fibonacci \#})(\text{second Fibonacci \#})}$$

II. Let's return to the Fibonacci quotients to learn what these numbers are converging on.

A. Recall how the Fibonacci sequence is generated, that is, by adding the two previous numbers to get the next one in the sequence.

B. Let's take a look at an example: $\frac{2}{1}$. We can rewrite the 2 on top as $1+1$, and the result is $1+\frac{1}{1}$.

C. The next example would be $\frac{3}{2}$. We can rewrite the 3 as $\frac{2+1}{2}$, or $1+\frac{1}{2}$. The fraction $\frac{1}{2}$ is the reciprocal of our first example, $\frac{2}{1}$. Thus, we can rewrite $\frac{3}{2}$ as $1+\cfrac{1}{1+\cfrac{1}{1}}$.

D. The quotient of any two consecutive Fibonacci numbers will result in this continued fraction, a continuing division of just the number 1.

E. This amazing pattern shows us an underlying structure that is not apparent from the definition of the Fibonacci numbers.

III. How can we use this discovery to lead us to the target, 1.618033988...?

A. If we take our discovery to the extreme, we see that the fractions just get longer and longer—forever.

$$\varphi = 1 + \cfrac{1}{\boxed{1+\cfrac{1}{1+\cfrac{1}{1+...}}}}$$

B. Let's consider a frame around the numbers (as shown in A. above) which we notice is equal to the original number. We'll call this original number φ. The framed expression is simply another copy of φ.

C. The algebraic equation for this number is $\varphi = 1 + \dfrac{1}{1}$ or

$\varphi = 1 + \dfrac{1}{\varphi}$. We can solve this equation and find that

$\varphi = \dfrac{1 + \sqrt{5}}{2} = 1.618033989\ldots$.

D. This number is called the *Golden Ratio*, which as we'll see in the next lecture, comes into play in geometry, art, and architecture.

IV. Let's close by returning to the Lucas numbers, which have the same generating process as the Fibonacci numbers but different starting, or seed, numbers.

A. The Lucas sequence starts with 2, 1—rather than 1, 1—and the generating process results in 2, 1, 3, 4, 7, 11, 18, 29, 47, 76, 123….

B. Even though the two sequences of numbers differ, do they have any common structure, given that the generating process is the same?

C. If we begin to look at the quotients of the Lucas numbers, we see that they, too, seem to be approaching the Golden Ratio.

D. We repeat the process that we used earlier of writing the quotients of consecutive Lucas numbers in terms of a continuing fraction. The results for the first few numbers are as follows:

$$\frac{4}{3} = 1 + \frac{1}{3} \qquad \frac{7}{4} = 1 + \cfrac{1}{1 + \cfrac{1}{3}} \qquad \frac{11}{7} = 1 + \cfrac{1}{1 + \cfrac{1}{1 + \cfrac{1}{3}}}$$

E. We see almost the identical pattern that we saw earlier, except that the last number is 3. However, if we continued the pattern into infinity, the 3 would drift off and we would see only the Golden Ratio.

F. In any kind of recurring sequence, no matter which two numbers we start with, all the quotients will approach the

Golden Ratio. The *process* is the essential feature of these sequences.

V. By simply looking at issues differently, and trying and making mistakes, we discover new worlds. Sir Francis Bacon said, "Truth comes out of error more easily than out of confusion."

Suggested Reading:

Edward B. Burger and Michael Starbird, *The Heart of Mathematics: An invitation to effective thinking*, Key College Publishing, Section 2.2, "Numerical Patterns in Nature: Discovering nature's beauty and the Fibonacci numbers."

Questions to Consider:

1. For each natural number given, express it as a sum of distinct, non-consecutive Fibonacci numbers: 52, 143, 12, 88.

2. Let's start with the numbers 0, 0, 1, and generate future numbers in our sequence by adding up the previous three numbers. Write out the first 15 terms in this sequence starting with the first 1. Use a calculator to evaluate the value of the quotients of consecutive terms (dividing the smaller term into the larger one). Do the quotients seem to be approaching a fixed number?

Lecture Five—Transcript
Sizing up the Fibonacci Numbers

Lewis Carroll once wrote: "It may well be doubted whether, in all the range of science, there is any field so fascinating to the explorer, so rich with hidden treasure, so fruitful in delightful surprises as pure mathematics."

Well, today, I want us to continue our journey through the wonderful sequence of numbers known as the Fibonacci numbers, and I want us to see further structure in that sequence of numbers. But the real-life lesson here in terms of thinking beyond mathematics is the importance of making mistakes and learning from those mistakes. Quite often in life, we feel that if we do something and it is wrong, we feel that we have somehow failed. Well, in reality, that failed attempt can, if we allow it, build insight into, in fact, a greater understanding of the situation that we are looking at.

In particular here, I want us to focus on the power of making mistakes, and learning from mistakes, and also, the power of just trying something, and from estimating, and making rough approximations. We can actually gain tremendous precision and discover new relationships, new understanding, and new structure, all from revisiting the Fibonacci numbers.

I'll remind you that the Fibonacci numbers, which we saw in the last lecture, was that collection of numbers, that sequence of numbers that we discovered organically by counting objects, in particular, spirals that we found in nature. And we saw this sequence that we built, which begins: 1, 1, 2, 3, 5, 8, 13, 21, 34, and so on, and we saw a tremendous amount of structure in that collection in terms of nature. Then, we even built the Lucas numbers, and so forth, and we saw that this is a natural sequence that Fibonacci named through the rabbits.

What I would like to do today is actually move from the Fibonacci numbers in nature, and actually explore the Fibonacci numbers for themselves. Now, the surprising thing here is that quite often, we see that when we move to the abstract world of mathematics, quite often, after we develop insights, we will actually see reflections of those insights in our everyday, ordinary world. So that again, we see this synergistic interplay between the abstract world of mathematics, which seems so foreign at first, and then, how it folds back into a better understanding of how we look, and in this case, how we see and perceive things. That's our goal for today; it is to try to better understand the structure of these special numbers in their own right.

Well, one thing we can do is just look at them and ask: What can we say about them? Well, if you look at those numbers, the first thing you might notice is that they are getting bigger, and for a good reason, because every time we produce the next number on the list, we're adding two previous numbers, and so therefore, these things are growing, and growing, and growing.

Well, once we see that these numbers are growing, we move from the qualitative to the quantitative, and we ask: How are they growing? Now, here's a great guess—maybe they're doubling each time, so that maybe the next one is twice as big as the previous one. Well, let's take a look and see if that's a good guess or not. It is certainly a guess, and all guesses are wonderful, but let's see if it accurately reports the nature of things.

If we take a look, we see that if you take 1, and double it, you do, indeed, get 2. That's a good start, so it's looking good. Unfortunately, though, if you take 2 and double it, you get 4, rather than the next Fibonacci number, which you will notice is 3, so that, now, in fact, we're a little bit off. If we continue, and if we take 3, and we double it, sadly, we don't get the 5. If we double 3, we get 6, so we've overshot yet again. If we take 5, and we double it, instead of getting 8, we're getting 10, so that we're overshooting even more. It's clear, then, that this natural, obvious guess wasn't correct, but this is a time to celebrate and to look deeper into the issue, rather than to retreat and feel that we somehow have done something bad. In fact, we've done something great, because we've taken an action, and that is so valuable.

In fact, let's take a look at the chart of numbers, and see exactly what happens. Let's look at this phenomenon a little closer. What we notice is that we if we look at 3, it's not quite the double of 2, which is 4, and what's the difference between the actual Fibonacci number and 2 times the previous one? Well, we see in that case that the difference is 1; $(2\times2)-3=1$. If we look at the next example, we see that the Fibonacci number 5 is not quite 2 times the previous one, which is 6; (3×2). The difference, you will see, again, is 1; $(3\times2)-5=1$.

Now, when we move to 8, what we see is that 8 is not quite 2 times 5, 5 being the previous Fibonacci number, because 2 times 5 is 10, and you will notice that the difference there is 2; $(2\times5)-8=2$. Let's keep going a little further and see if we see a recognizable pattern.

If we look at the next Fibonacci number 13, we see that it is not quite twice the previous one, because twice the previous one would be 2 times 8, and 2 times 8 is 16; if we look at the difference between 16 and 13, we see 3; $(2\times8)-13=3$.

Well, now, if you look at the differences, you might start noticing something. The differences are 1, 1, 2, 3, and maybe, now, you're beginning to realize that that is the familiar prelude to a now very important sequence. In particular, if we keep going, let's take a look at 21. 21 is not quite 2 times the previous Fibonacci number, which is 13; 2 times 13 is 26. 21 is not quite 26. It is off by 5. Well, this is a confirmatory observation.

We see that these differences are, in fact, the Fibonacci numbers themselves, so that by making this mistake, we actually uncover some amazing, wonderful structure. We see that, in fact, if you take a particular Fibonacci number, and then look at it and take twice the previous one, the difference between those two numbers is going to be a Fibonacci number, and in fact, you can actually say this in a sort of formulaic way, if you wanted to. You could actually use this to build Fibonacci numbers, because you can do it as follows: You can say that to find the next Fibonacci number, here's the process. You take 2 times the previous Fibonacci number, and then subtract off the Fibonacci number that came twice before the last one.

2 x the next Fibonacci number

– the Fibonacci number two before the last

the next Fibonacci number

Now, let me actually give an example so that you can see how this really does work. Suppose you want to find the next Fibonacci number after 13. What do you do? You double 13, which we know is too big, and that's going to be 26. Then, what do we subtract? We subtract the Fibonacci number that is two before 13. One before 13 is 8, and before that is 5, so we subtract 5, and here's what happens. We have 2 times 13, which is 26, minus 5, which is 21;

(2×13)–5=21. That's the next Fibonacci number after 13. Here's a way of actually generating the Fibonacci numbers, and we found that by actually making a mistake. That's fantastic. The mistakes are, in fact, valuable and important, and they provide us with deep insights into discovery.

Okay, well, we can look at things in a different way, and I want to have us actually think about looking at the difference, and how these Fibonacci numbers are, in fact, growing not just by subtracting and doubling, but by comparing them in some more fundamental way. In fact, one way to compare numbers is just to see how they are relative to each other. And in fact, that's where the word "ratio" comes from, by looking at, and comparing two numbers, and dividing one into the other, and seeing how they compare.

Thus, in fact, another way of looking at the issue—which is a wonderful thing, by the way, as a life thinking strategy—is to look at issues from several points of view. Once you have one perspective, it's always wonderful, and sometimes extremely valuable, to force ourselves to look at it from a different perspective, a different vantage point, and again, we reveal hidden structure, new insights.

In this case, then, instead of subtracting and doubling, let's actually take a look at how these numbers are growing by looking at how they are growing relative to each other, by looking at the ratio, the quotient, of two consecutive Fibonacci numbers. In particular, then, I want us to look at how the fractions—one Fibonacci number divided by the previous one—how those fractions change.

Let's take a look. What we see, when we look at a table that we can build, we will just start taking Fibonacci numbers and dividing one into the previous one. For example, the first one we can look at is to take 2 and divide it by 1. Those are two consecutive Fibonacci numbers. If we divide them, we see that of course, the answer is 2. We take the next pair, 2 and 3, and divide 2 into 3. We see 1.5. If we take 5 divided by 3, we get 1.666, repeating forever. If we look at 8 divided by 5, we see 1.6; 13 divided by 8, we see 1.625. We can now scroll down and see a lot of these that you can just compute on a calculator. For example, 89 over 55 is 1.6181818, forever. If you scroll down a little further, in fact a lot further, you will find two consecutive Fibonacci numbers. One is 1597, and if we divide it by the previous one, which is 987, we see the decimal 1.618034448, and so on. Let's do one more. If we do the very next pair, we see 2584, a pretty big Fibonacci number, divided by the previous one, 1597, and that decimal works out to be 1.618033813, and so on.

Well, when we look at this long list of decimals, something is striking. In particular, we see that as we move on down this list, the decimal number seems to be actually approaching something. Those fractions are getting closer and closer to each other, for they seem to be converging, if you will, on the number 1.61803 something, so that they actually seem to be coming together.

Now, how can we realize this observation in a more dramatic way? Well, actually, there's a wonderful puzzle paradox that I want to share with you right now, where we can really begin to build some insight into exactly what is going on with this phenomenon, where these quotients seem to be heading toward some fixed number. The fractions are getting closer together.

Well, if we take look at this puzzle here, which you will see is that I actually have a square, and it turns out that square is in fact eight units by eight units, so that its eight units high, and it is eight units long. If you were to actually compute the area of this, you would see that it is 8×8, or 8^2, and you would see the number 64. That's the total amount of the area of the square.

Now, certainly, the area would not be changed if I were to just move the pieces of the square around a little bit. If I move the pieces of the square around, you'll notice that there are, in fact, a bunch of pieces. Let me just show you them. Here's a piece that is actually 8 on this side, and this side here is actually 3. This piece here—which is a little bit strange looking, and is actually, I guess, an example of a trapezoid, but who cares?—is actually 1, 2, 3, 4, 5 here, by 1, 2, 3, 4, 5, so this is 5 by 5, and this bottom part here is 1, 2, 3, so that they all have different lengths.

We can actually move these puzzle pieces around, and let's see what happens if we do that. I'm going to slide this over here for a second, and I'm deliberately keeping all the pieces on the easel. I don't want you to think that this is somehow a sleight of hand, where I am actually removing some of the pieces and replacing them with other pieces. These are the same puzzle pieces. You'll see that they fit together perfectly on the 3 along the 3, and then this puzzle piece right here, I am going to move up to here, and here, and they match perfectly. Then, I'm just going to lower it down onto here, and now, I have a rectangle.

Now, let's compute the area of the rectangle. Now remember, before, when the pieces were rearranged in a square, the area was 64. Let see what the area of this is. Well, this is 1, 2, 3, 4, 5. It is 5 by 1, 2, 3, 4, 5, 6, 7, 8, 9, 10, 11, 12, 13. It's 5 by 13, but 5 by 13 is actually 65; $5 \times 13 = 65$.

Now, wait a minute. How could the area of this actually be 65, when before, when they were reconfigured, the area was 64? It seems as though I've built some area just by moving the pieces around. Well, this is indeed a paradox, because if this were really true, then you could just buy a little, teeny plot of land, and move the land around, and all of a sudden, have hundreds of thousands of acres, and you'd own all of America, and you would be very, very wealthy, and I hope you'll remember me, one of your teachers.

Anyway, obviously, something is wrong here, and the paradox can be seen if we return to the picture. Actually, make the edges line up absolutely perfectly straight. I'm going to lower this down, and I want you to watch very carefully. Now, the corners are meeting, and if you look at that, do you see what's happening? The corners meat, but you see that there's actually a black region right down the diagonal? That black region right down the diagonal actually has a bit of area, and that area is actually one unit. So there's the extra unit of area. It's that the pieces don't fit together perfectly, but they're so close, they're just off by one.

Well, in fact, this puzzle paradox actually allows us to devise a really amazing formula, an amazing formula, in fact, that relates the quotient of the Fibonacci numbers. In particular, what we see is that if you take three Fibonacci numbers, a first Fibonacci number, a second Fibonacci number, and a third Fibonacci number, three in a row—in this case, we looked at 5, 8, and 13—and in this example, what did we see? What we saw was that if you take the middle one, 8, and square it, 64, it's going to be off by 1 from the product of the flanking Fibonacci numbers, in this case, 5 by 13; $(5 \times 13) - 8^2 = 1$.

It turns out that that phenomenon is always true, so in particular, if you take a look at the middle Fibonacci number, and square it, and subtract off the product of the first and the last Fibonacci numbers, then that difference will be either plus or minus 1.

$$\frac{\text{middle Fibonacci \#}}{\text{first Fibonacci \#}} - \frac{\text{last Fibonacci \#}}{\text{middle Fibonacci \#}} = \pm \frac{1}{\left(\text{first Fibonacci \#}\right)\left(\text{second Fibonacci \#}\right)}$$

If you do some division, you can actually rewrite that mathematical fact, and actually express it as the middle Fibonacci number divided by the first Fibonacci number, minus the last Fibonacci number, divided by the middle Fibonacci number. So the difference of the two consecutive quotients of Fibonacci numbers is going to actually be getting very, very small. It is going to equal plus or minus 1 divided by the first Fibonacci number times the second Fibonacci number.

As the Fibonacci numbers grow, then, we see through this paradox, that is, numbers must be getting closer together. What, in fact, are they getting towards? That is the question. Well, to see that, we should try to look at these things in a different way. Let's return to the quotients, but look at the quotients in a different way.

In particular, let's return to the idea of how these numbers were generated: by adding the two previous to get the next one. In fact, let's actually take a look at an example, say, 2 divided by 1, $\frac{2}{1}$.

Well, we can actually rewrite that 2 on top as 1 plus 1, $1 + 1$. And if I do that, then I can actually write the fraction 2 over 1 as just 1 plus 1, or, if I wanted to, 1 plus 1 over 1, $\frac{2}{1} = 1 + 1 = 1 + \frac{1}{1}$. Well, that doesn't seem to be too useful, but you will notice that all we see there are 1s.

Let's move onto the next one, 3 over 2, $\frac{3}{2}$. If we look at 3 over 2, and we write that out, we can express the 3 as 2 plus 1, $\frac{2+1}{2}$. And if we look at 2 plus 1, and divide it by 2, what do we see? What I see is $1 + \frac{1}{2}$. Well, but, $\frac{1}{2}$ is precisely the reciprocal, or the flip of what we just did, namely, 2 over 1. I could actually write, then, 3 over 2 as

1 plus 1 over 1 plus 1 over 1, $\dfrac{3}{2}$ as $1 + \dfrac{1}{1 + \dfrac{1}{1}}$. That is sort of a mouthful, but you can see it on the screen, and you can just see that it's a fraction within a fraction within a fraction. In fact, if you keep trying this, you see that the pattern continues, so that in particular, if you take the quotient of two consecutive Fibonacci numbers, what you are going to see is a continued fraction, a fraction within fraction within fraction, of 1 plus 1 over 1 plus 1 over 1 plus 1 over, and so forth, until you get down to that last one.

This is an incredibly surprising discovery, and for mathematicians, this is an amazing breakthrough, because now we are seeing some hidden structure that was by no means obvious or apparent by looking at how the Fibonacci numbers were defined, and yet, we see that if we look at the quotients of any two consecutive 1s, we can express them just as a long, continued division of just the number one. Again, fantastic structure.

Well, in fact, this fantastic structure is sort of amazing, because it's a defining trait. There are no other fractions except for quotients of Fibonacci numbers that have this feature of being expressed just in terms of one. This is a really, really special discovery.

Now, how can we use that to lead us to the target of that number, 1.618...? Well, all we have to do is take this to the extreme. As we continue to look at these quotients, what happens to these fractions? They are just getting longer, and longer, and longer, so that we see 1 plus 1 over 1 plus 1 over 1 plus 1 over, and so forth. If we were to see the target, we would just do this forever, and so we would have this infinite list of 1 plus 1, over 1 plus 1, over 1 plus 1, over 1 plus 1, over 1, forever.

How can we figure out what that long, complicated-looking number actually is? Well, there's actually a way of doing that, and here's what I want us to do. Imagine putting a frame, a frame around the inner 1 plus 1 over 1 plus 1 over 1, just as you see there. If you just look at that frame, and look at it closely, you see that it's nothing more than just the original number again, for we just see this infinitely long list of 1 plus 1, over 1 plus 1, over 1, forever.

If we call that original number *phi*, the Greek letter phi (φ), then, we see in fact that the boxed-in expression in fact, is simply another copy of phi.

$$\varphi = 1 + \cfrac{1}{\boxed{1 + \cfrac{1}{1 + \cfrac{1}{1 + \dots}}}}$$

Thus, from this infinitely long process, we can produce an actual closed algebraic equation, and the algebraic equation, which I will just say, is phi equals 1 plus 1 over itself, $\varphi = 1 + \dfrac{1}{1}$, or phi equals 1 plus 1 over phi, $\varphi = 1 + \dfrac{1}{\varphi}$. Now, we can actually use algebra to solve that. In fact, if you are fan of the quadratic formula, you can actually solve it, and you'll see that you get two answers, and we are looking for the positive one. We discover that phi is the number 1 plus the square root of 5, all divided by 2, $\varphi = \dfrac{1 + \sqrt{5}}{2}$.

Now, that seems like sort of a strange, weird number, but all we have to do, in fact, is look at that number on a calculator. If we type in 5 and hit the square root key, add 1, and then take the whole thing and divide it by 2, what would you see? You would see 1.618033989, and so forth. We see, again, the decimal that these fractions are heading toward.

Now, though, we can express that infinitely long collection of 1s in a very tight expression, just 1 plus the square root of 5, over 2. This is a wonderful thing that mathematicians love to do. Mathematicians love to take something that is sort of unwieldy, but somehow natural, and see if they can re-express it in a different way.

In this case, we have this wonderful, beautiful expression of just a long list of 1s being divided by itself, which is quite pretty, and I would argue, aesthetic in its own right, and what we are doing is that were bringing some mathematical principles into play, and we see that that infinite process can be expressed in a sort of finite statement. That finite statement costs something. There's no such thing as a mathematical free lunch. If you have an infinitely long, complicated sort of list of 1s, if you are going to rewrite it in a different way, that rewritten expression should be complicated as well, and in this case, we see that sort of square root, that threatening square root symbol there. It turns out that we are able to produce this very, very tight expression for this wonderful, beautiful run of 1s dividing, dividing, dividing.

We have this number 1 plus the square root of 5, over 2, $\dfrac{1+\sqrt{5}}{2}$, which we have already seen in its decimal form can be expressed as 1.61803398, and it goes on forever. This number, in fact, is called the *Golden Ratio*, and it is an extremely famous number. I must editorialize, if you will allow me. My research interests in mathematics are, actually in number theory, in precisely the kinds of questions that Mike and I have been talking about so far in these lectures, although I am trying to prove theorems that have yet to be proven, so I am trying to discover new truths. A lot of time, though, people see me on the street, and when they find out that I do number theory, they say, "Gee, Ed, what's your favorite number?"—thinking that they can use it to gamble on, or to play on the roulette wheel, and so forth—and I tell them, "It's not seven, and it's not three. It's 1 plus the square root of 5, over 2." It is this Golden Ratio.

Now, why is it my favorite number? Well, first of all, because it is the only number that can be expressed in this infinite process of quotients dividing, dividing, dividing, just using 1s, just using 1s. As a number theorist, I find that exceptionally beautiful.

Actually, though, I'm foreshadowing what we're going to be doing our next lecture, where we are actually going to be looking at geometry and art, and actually thinking about the idea of aesthetics. The question is, maybe mathematics and aesthetics somehow go together, and we will see an interface through this Golden Ratio.

In fact, then, as this lecture is the last lecture where we focus on numbers, we're going to be moving to the next round, where we are going to be thinking about the geometric visual world. That's an excitement, a little enticement that I want to plant in the backs of our heads right now. This Golden Ratio, which is my favorite number, I hope to entice you with in the next two lectures on geometry, and have you see, that, in fact, it is potentially a candidate for your favorite number.

Well, we have this number—1 plus the square root of 5, over 2—which, maybe, you don't like the sound of, so maybe the decimal is better, 1.6180339, and so forth, but in any case, we have this special number, the number that in fact these quotients of Fibonacci numbers want to move to. The quotients are drawn to this particular number, and that is sort of amazing.

I want to close now by returning to the Lucas numbers. Remember that those are the numbers that have the exact same process as the Fibonacci numbers. The generating process is the same. We just taken the two previous people and add them to get the next person on our list. The only difference is in the starting seeds. Instead of starting with 1,1, to generate and build the Fibonacci numbers, here, Lucas started with the numbers 2, 1. By adding those two, we got 3, and then adding 1 and 3, we got 4, and we produced the Lucas sequence of numbers, which is 2, 1, 3, 4, 7, 11, 18, 29, and so forth, as we saw in the last lecture. You might recall that at the very end of the last lecture, I raised the question that even though those numbers don't agree, namely that the Lucas sequence and the Fibonacci sequence differ after the first few numbers, is there any common structure given that, in fact, the generating process is the same?

Well, now we know exactly how to look at this. We simply look at the quotients, and see how they are growing. When we do that with the Lucas numbers, let's see what happens. If we take 1 and divide it by 2, we see 0.5. If we take 3 and divide it by 1, we see the number 3; so that so far, we have gone from 0.5 to 3. That's a sort of wild change in number size, but then 4 divided by 3 is 1.333 forever; 7 divided by 4 is 1.75—and so again, we are fluctuating a little bit—11 divided by 7 is 1.571; 18 divided by 11 is 1.636363 forever; 29 divided by 18 is 1.61111.

Notice what's happening. We seem to actually be heading toward the 1.618033, and so forth. Let's go down a little bit further, and you see if we jump down to 123 divided by 76, we see 1.61884210, and all of a sudden, we say, "Wait a minute. Maybe, in fact, the Lucas sequence is conforming; as you do it longer and longer, and compare the relative sizes by taking the quotients of consecutive Lucas numbers, maybe, in fact, they are heading toward this Golden Ratio, Ed's favorite number."

Well, in fact, we can absolutely see that, and the way that we can see it is by doing the same process that we did before. Let's see if we can write the quotients of consecutive Lucas numbers in terms of a fraction that goes on, and look what we see. If you take 4 divided by 3, we get 1 plus 1/3. If we take 7 divided by 4, we see 1 plus 1 over 1 plus 1 over 3. If we take 11 divided by 7—this is the last one we will look at—we see 1 plus 1 over 1 plus 1 over 1 plus 1 over 3. In particular, we see the exact same pattern. However, instead of having all 1s, the very last number is always a 3. If we did the process forever, though, what would happen to that last three? It would keep drifting further, and further, and further off to infinity, and if we just did it forever, the 3 would disappear, and we would just see that 1 plus 1 over 1 plus 1 over 1 plus 1 over 1 plus 1 over 1, forever, which, of course, you may recall, is the Golden Ratio. It's the 1 plus the square of 5, over 2.

What's the amazing realization? The realization is that if you have any kind of recurring sequence—meaning, just take the rule of adding the two previous people in order to generate the next person on the list, and then repeat that process—then, no matter which two numbers you start with, no matter what your starting seeds—pick them big, pick them small—it doesn't matter. In fact, if you look at the relative sizes, they are all going to approach the Golden Ratio: 1 plus the square root of 5, over 2; 1.618033 and so forth.

Well, this is an amazing discovery, because what we see is that even though quotients might deviate wildly at the beginning, they all settle down. What do we see? We see that, in fact, all of these roads lead to the Golden Ratio. It's sort of amazing. It doesn't matter what the numbers are at all. It's the process. Now, we're actually focusing in on the essential feature of these sequences. In fact, it wasn't the 1, 1 that we started with to build the Fibonacci numbers. It wasn't the 2, 1 that we used as the starting seed in order to build the Lucas numbers. We could start with 17 and 5, or we could start with 144 and -2, but if we just adopt that process of generating the next one by adding the previous two to get the next one, and do that, then the growth, in fact, those quotients, are going to conform to the Golden Ratio.

We see, then, in fact, that all of these sequences, all of these, lead to the Golden Ratio. Not only is this Golden Ratio my favorite number, 1 plus 1 over 1 plus 1, etc., forever, it's kind of beautiful, because we see hidden structure that was not at all visible when we were thinking about the Golden Ratio in terms of just the Fibonacci numbers. It came apart by actually expressing the 1 plus 1 over 1 plus 1 over 1, etc.

Now, in fact, we see that there's actually beauty in that funny-looking number, and the question I want to close with now is: Now that we have sensed some beauty, maybe we can actually see reflections of that beauty in other walks of life, not just in numbers, but in the visual world, and in particular, our world. By simply just looking at issues differently, and trying and making mistakes, we actually uncover new worlds. I am actually reminded of the words of Sir Francis Bacon, when he wrote: "Truth comes out of error more easily than out of confusion." The power of making mistakes.

In the next lecture, we will take up the visual world of geometry, and see if we can see reflections of the Golden Ratio there.

Lecture Six
The Sexiest Rectangle

Edward B. Burger, Ph.D.

Scope:

Our mathematical travels thus far have led us to develop a sense of mathematical aesthetics. Now we wonder if mathematics can be used to illuminate structure behind the aesthetics of art and nature. We begin with a basic question of grace and proportion: What are the dimensions of the most attractive rectangle—the rectangle we envision when we close our eyes on a dark starry night and dream of beauty? That rectangle is referred to as the *Golden Rectangle*, famed for its role in art, architecture, and even music. Its aesthetic appeal may well arise from elegant mathematical principles that generate its pleasing proportion. In this lecture, we will explore this attractive geometric shape and discover a precise manner to construct a Golden Rectangle with just a straight edge and a compass.

Outline

I. In this lecture, we turn to the world of geometry and begin to make connections between mathematics and art.

   A. We begin by asking: What is the most pleasing rectangle that we can imagine? Many people instinctively choose the *Golden Rectangle* as the most aesthetically pleasing example.

   B. The term *Golden Rectangle* might remind us of the Golden Ratio from the last lecture.

   C. Indeed, a Golden Rectangle is defined as a rectangle in which the length of the base divided by the length of the height is equal to the Golden Ratio.

   D. We see Golden Rectangles everywhere, such as in an index card. Remember that the dimensions of an index card are 3×5. These are two consecutive Fibonacci numbers, the quotient of which will approach the Golden Ratio.

II. Let's look at some examples of Golden Rectangles throughout the art and architecture of humanity.

   A. The Parthenon exhibits the most famous architectural appearance of the proportions of the Golden Rectangle.

B. Those same ratios appear in Grecian eyecups.

C. When we look back at these ancient appearances of the Golden Rectangle, we are left with the unanswered question of whether those proportions appear through specific intent or by sheer chance.

D. During the Renaissance, Leonardo da Vinci and others were definitely aware of the proportions of the Golden Rectangle.

    1. The figure in da Vinci's unfinished portrait of St. Jerome seems to be positioned in a Golden Rectangle.

    2. da Vinci wrote a treatise on the Golden Ratio called *The Divine Proportion.*

E. In the 19th century, the French Impressionists explored scientific ideas in their art.

    1. Georges Seurat was a leading Impressionist painter who tried to incorporate mathematical and scientific concepts in his work.

    2. In Seurat's painting *La Parade*, we see a number of Golden Rectangles deliberately placed.

F. Returning to architecture, we can look for Golden Rectangles in the work of Le Corbusier, who believed that human life was soothed by mathematical ideas.

III. How can we mathematically construct a Golden Rectangle?

    A. We can build a Golden Rectangle using the techniques of the ancient Greeks with simply a straight edge and a compass.

        1. We begin with a perfect square and extend the line of its base.

        2. We place the tip of the compass at the midpoint of the base of the square.

        3. We next extend the other end of the compass to the northeast corner of the square.

        4. From there, we draw an arc that intersects the extension of the base we drew earlier.

        5. We extend the top of the square as we did the base, then draw a perpendicular line to the point at which the arc intersected the extended base.

        6. The resulting rectangle is a perfect Golden Rectangle.

    B. Returning to the original square, we can use the Pythagorean theorem to verify mathematically that our construction is a Golden Rectangle. In fact, we find that our Golden

Rectangle exhibits the proportions of the Golden Ratio, that is $\dfrac{1+\sqrt{5}}{2}$.

C. The right triangle in our construction, which we used to verify the Golden Rectangle, is sometimes called the *Golden Triangle*. It is defined as a triangle in which the height is twice the base.
   1. We can produce any triangle by arranging four reduced copies of the original triangle.
   2. For the Golden Triangle, the same process can be repeated with five reduced copies.

IV. In this lecture, we have seen mathematics reflected in issues of aesthetics.

A. The question remains whether the reflections of mathematics we see in works of art are deliberate.

B. Is it possible that mathematics underlies the works of art that we find aesthetically appealing?

C. We'll close this lecture with an example of the Golden Rectangle in the musical work of Claude Debussy.
   1. Debussy was fascinated with the Golden Rectangle and Golden Ratio and tried to capture these proportions in his musical work.
   2. If we analyze the structure of Debussy's prelude to *The Afternoon of a Faun*, we can pinpoint Fibonacci numbers in its musical phrasing.
   3. Debussy even approached the Golden Ratio in the timing of certain sections of his work.

D. Aesthetics and mathematics are deeply related. There is mathematics in beauty and beauty in mathematics. The Golden Rectangle is one of the most visible shapes that appear in artistic creations throughout the ages. In the next lecture, we'll look further at the self-regeneration properties of the Golden Rectangle and Golden Triangle, which might explain why these shapes are so appealing.

Suggested Reading:

Edward B. Burger and Michael Starbird, *The Heart of Mathematics: An invitation to effective thinking*, Key College Publishing, Section

4.3, "The Sexiest Rectangle: Finding aesthetics in life, art, and math through the Golden Rectangle."

Questions to Consider:

1. Draw a rectangle with its longer edge as the base (it could be a square, it could be a long and skinny rectangle...whatever you like, but we suggest that you do *not* draw a Golden Rectangle). Now using the top edge of the rectangle, draw the square just above the rectangle so that the square's base is the top edge of the rectangle. You have now produced a large new rectangle (the original rectangle together with this square sitting above it). Now attach a square to the right of this rectangle so that the square's left side is the right edge of the large rectangle. You've constructed an even larger rectangle. Now repeat this procedure—that is, append on the top of this huge rectangle the largest square you can and follow that move by attaching the largest square you can to the right of the resulting rectangle. Start with a small rectangle near the bottom left corner of a page and continue this process as much as you can on the page. Now measure the dimensions of the largest rectangle you've built and divide the longer side by the shorter one. How does that ratio compare to the Golden Ratio? Experiment with various starting rectangles. What do you notice about the ratios?

2. Consider a 10x10 grid. Find the four dots that when joined to make a horizontal rectangle, make a rectangle that is the closest approximation to a Golden Rectangle. (*Challenge*: What if the rectangle need not be horizontal?)

Lecture Six—Transcript
The Sexiest Rectangle

Well, for the past few lectures, we've been exploring the world of numbers and quantity, and looking at the hidden structure of both within the numbers and reflections within our own everyday world.

Now, we're about to embark on the next major chapter in this course, which is the visual world of geometry, which, believe it or not, parallels the enticement and the intrigue of numbers. We will begin this journey, in fact, with a look at aesthetics, our own tastes, and wonder, if, in fact, aesthetics can somehow be connected with mathematical thinking. In this lecture, we will see that in fact, there are rich connections if we open our minds to explore them.

John Keats once wrote: "What the imagination seizes as beauty must be truth—whether it existed before or not."

In this lecture, I want us to actually consider beauty as a mathematical possibility. In particular, I want to begin with the following strange question: What do you think of when you think of the sexiest rectangle? Well, what is a sexy rectangle? What I mean by that is the rectangle that you envision in your mind's eye when you close your eyes, and think of a rectangle, and the ideal proportions. It probably wouldn't be very, very, very long, not very high, and it probably wouldn't be very square-like. It probably would be something in between.

In fact, here are four possibilities I want you to look at. Now, look at these four rectangles and ask yourself, "Which rectangle captures the spirit of rectangle-ness in my eye? If I were to close my eyes, and think of a rectangle, which of these four comes closest to that rectangle?"

Well, you have your guess, and it turns out that many people like the second rectangle from the left. The second rectangle from the left seems to draw the attention of many, many people. Now, I must tell you that if we actually did an election, we might have another run-off situation, and we might have to go back to Florida and Dade County, and it might be a mess, because it's not absolutely clear-cut, but certainly, a plurality of people tend to like that second rectangle.

Well, that second rectangle, actually, it's called the *Golden Rectangle*. Well, Golden Rectangle might conjure up images from our previous lecture of the Golden Ratio, and in fact, there's good reason for that. For a rectangle to be a Golden Rectangle, the very definition of that is somehow comparing the length of the base to the length of the height. In particular, we define a rectangle to be a Golden Rectangle if you take the length of the base, and divide by the length of the height. That quotient, that ratio, will be the Golden Ratio, that special number—1 plus the square root of 5, all divided by 2—which in decimal form is 1.6180338998, and so on, and it goes on. You can plug it in the calculator; that number that happens to be my favorite number. We're going to see it again. Coincidence? I think not. I like the number, and it turns out, it appears throughout the dawn of humanity all the way through humanity's history, so in fact, maybe humanity finds this number to be interesting.

Well, the Golden Rectangle—and here, I actually happen to have one for you to see; the proportions of the base to the height of this in fact conform to the Golden Ratio—is a very attractive rectangle, and we have actually seen these things. In fact, you see them all the time at work or at home if you're doing hobbies. If you look at the dimensions of an index card, you will see that they are actually very close; if you take the base to the height; it closely conforms to the Golden Ratio.

Surprising? Well, no, because what are the dimensions of this? You know what the dimensions of an index card are. They are 3 by 5, and notice that 3 and 5 are consecutive Fibonacci numbers. Certainly, then, that ratio must be close to the Golden Ratio, since we have already seen, in the previous lecture, that as you go down and look at the quotients of consecutive Fibonacci numbers, they do approach this special Golden Ratio, so that this is a very attractive rectangle.

In fact, you may say, "Gee, isn't that a coincidence?" Well, I would argue not. I think that Madison Avenue knows how alluring we find these, and how attractive they are, and that's why we keep buying them. Do you notice that you keep buying these index cards? Maybe the reason you buy them is not because of their utility, but maybe because you're drawn to the beautiful proportions of that rectangle. Well, okay, maybe you actually use them.

Well, there are a lot of examples of the Golden Rectangle outside of the humorous possibility of looking at the 3 by 5 index card, and I wanted us to take a look at some of the examples of the Golden

Rectangle all throughout the art and the architectural history of humanity. Let's start, in fact, with the ancient Greeks.

Now, if you take a look at this image, you, of course, immediately recognize it to be the Parthenon. Now, you might say, "Oh, okay, Ed, if I draw a rectangle from that horizontal line that we see on top, down to the bottom, and so forth, and it sweeps out a rectangle, that is a Golden Rectangle?" I might hear you wonder that. It turns out that the answer is "no." It's not, because this thing is in ruins. They sort of let it run down, and go downhill, and maybe it should be under new management, or something. At one time, though, it was very fancy, and in particular, it had a roof. How decadent.

Now, if you imagine extrapolating that roof line back in, and take a look at it with the roof line in, then you can draw in a perfect Golden Rectangle. You can see how beautifully it conforms to the Parthenon, which leads us to wonder whether, in fact, that was intentional or unintentional, or just random. But there you see an example of an image that very closely conforms with the Golden Rectangle. We'll come back to this issue of whether it's there or not, in fact, in a few minutes.

Let's move on to another example from ancient Greece. Let's look at the object known as a Grecian eyecup. You can see this cup; it sort of has the two eyes looking at it, and so it sort of has the right name, and if you look at the various proportions and dimensions of this thing, you see that if you measure, in some sense, from one end of the handle into the cup itself, if we call that length one-half, then, in fact, the entire height is very nearly a perfect Golden Ratio—1 plus the square root of 5, over 2—and you can see in the figure many exemplars of the Golden Ratio appearing, and thus producing objects and relations that conform to the Golden Rectangle, so we see more examples of this.

Now, is it intentional or not? Well, actually, no one knows. We do not know if the Greeks deliberately allowed the Golden Rectangle to inform their art and architecture, or whether it's coincidence, or whether it perhaps just happens to be random, and that, in fact, since we can't measure things with infinite precision, it's close, but not exactly the Golden Rectangle.

Well, no one does know, and you can have your own opinion, but it would seem certainly to be more romantic to think that in fact maybe they did this subconsciously, where they just picked a ratio, proportions that seemed particularly attractive, and that attractive one seems to conform to the Golden Rectangle. We do not know for sure at this point, though, the answer to whether it was deliberate or not.

If we move ahead a little bit in human history, move to the Renaissance, Leonardo da Vinci definitely was conscious of the Golden Rectangle and the Golden Ratio. In fact, as an example, we should take a look here at the unfinished portrait of St. Jerome. Now, here what we see is a figure, St. Jerome, and he is sort of sitting down, and his right arm is extended in, but if you were to draw a perfect Golden Rectangle around the figure itself, what you see is that it beautifully conforms with everything: How the head is tilted down, the very bottom of the toe and the right hand edge where the elbow on the left arm is. You can see that it conforms quite nicely, and so maybe, in fact, what we are seeing here is a perfect Golden Rectangle.

Well, deliberate or otherwise—we don't know for sure if he deliberately tried to capture that, or if that rectangular shape just seemed to be attractive to him, and he was trying to capture it. If you look closely at that rectangle that we superimposed on the image, you'll notice that it doesn't perfectly conform. Look at the left-hand side, and notice that that left-hand side, for example, doesn't actually touch the body, doesn't even touch that lower part of the cape that is draped there. It is sort of just dangling out there for no reason at all except to make it a perfect Golden Rectangle. Is there a Golden Rectangle there or not? Well, technically, I guess the figure is not one, but notice how closely it does conform to one. And then there's a question of whether, in fact, that was just an aesthetic deliberate appearance of it, or if, in fact, this really was something that was intentional, to bring in this mathematical object, this mathematical structure.

It is known, by the way, that Leonardo did know about the Golden Ratio and the Golden Rectangle, because he actually illustrated a book on the subject. The book's title was *De Devina Proportione*, which actually means "the divine proportion," which is another phrase that we use sometimes for the Golden Ratio. Thus, he certainly knew about these objects, and in fact, there's a famous illustration where you can see various features that are trying to capture part of those relations.

If we move further through the art history, we come to the Impressionism era in France, and here, of course, the artists and scientists were having a very exciting moment in history, where people were coming together and sharing, and exploring ideas. Georges Seurat is a wonderful example of an artist who really embraced these mathematical ideas and tried to incorporate these concepts deliberately in his works. In fact, it is said that Seurat actually attacked every canvas with the Golden Rectangle, very intentionally. Here, in this painting, *La Parade*, we in fact see many Golden Rectangles. In fact, you can see, glowing, three different Golden Rectangles in the work, very deliberately placed. And in fact, if you take their actual lengths and divide one by the other you actually will get the perfect Golden Ratio. In particular, if you take the length that you see right there, and divide it by this length, then, in fact, you have the ratio that is a perfect Golden Ratio. Similarly, if you take that length and divide it by this length, you have another example of that.

If we return to architecture but move forward a bit, the French architect Le Corbusier is an architect who actually believes that human life is soothed by mathematical ideas, rather than pained by them as so many people in society believe. So he actually tried to incorporate the Golden Rectangle in his works. Here, we're looking at a drawing of a French villa that he designed several years ago, many years ago, and you can see that if you draw a rectangle around the villa all the way up to the very top of the roof, you can see that the roof extends from the chimney all the way down to the bottom. That's a perfect Golden Rectangle, and it's a rectangle that actually, in fact, was done deliberately. So it was deliberately placed there to try to make that environment more aesthetically appealing and interesting.

If this were one of those infomercials, this might be the time where I would say, "Okay, now I know you're sold, how do I order one? Where's the 900 number, or the 800 number to call, to actually own my own Golden Rectangle?" Well, of course, this is actually a class on great thinking and great mathematics, so there will be no 800 number. However, the question of how you actually construct, how you actually mathematically build a Golden Rectangle is a question that is worth asking, and one that I would like us to consider.

In fact, you can actually build one of these using the techniques of the ancient Greeks, where they simply used a straight edge and a compass to actually make geometric constructions. I'm going to actually build you the Golden Rectangle, and will give you a method for building your own Golden Rectangle, if you want to build one, and this is going to be a perfect Golden Rectangle.

First, we begin with a perfect square, and that is easy to construct. You can actually do that with a straight edge and compass if you want to, although I won't do that right now. We start with a square, though, and remember that the only rules that we have, in fact, are straight-edged, unmarked. The Greeks did not like the straight edge to be marked. We also have a compass. Well, okay, I don't have a compass here that's big enough, so I'm going to use a pin with a string, and I can make images that will capture arcs of circles. This is what a compass does, so, in fact, we'll just think of this as my compass.

Here is the recipe for producing a Golden Rectangle, and this is going to be a construction, so of course, it's going to be a work in progress. The first thing that we do is we extend the length of this square base a little bit. Now, I am going to tell you right now that I'm going to overshoot, so this is going to be something where we want to actually erase things, you see? I'm doing it right now just for us, though, so I'm going to extend this line a bit, let's say, out to here, so that I have sort of a little runway, now, here.

Now, I take my compass, and I find the precise midpoint of this square. The precise midpoint looks like it's right around here, and I put the sharp, dangerous part of my compass right in there, and so that is at the midpoint, and then I bring the compass up so that it lines up perfectly with this corner of the square, and what I'm going to do is that I'm going to now draw an arc that goes down. First, then, let me just put in that line where I'm going to extend, so that you can see it clearly. That's where I am going to start. Then, when I produce this, I'm going to do this live, so wish me luck. I hope you're thinking curvy thoughts right now.

Here we go. I'm going to create an arc of a circle, and then I'm just going to make the arc of the circle until I hit the runway, so I am going to go to the runway, and I stop. Now, that intersected the runway somewhere. I can now remove this compass. Now, what I am going to do is extend this length, and then just draw a perpendicular from where the arc of the circle intersected the runway, up to this line. If I do that—let's see if I can do this with some care—then, in fact, the object that I have within this border, well, I want you to look at it. Are you beginning to get a little rectangularly excited? Well, in fact, this is a perfect Golden Rectangle, and maybe to illustrate that, let me bring up that Golden Rectangle from before. Let me just show you that, in fact, we can superimpose it pretty much right on target. Of course, you've got to be able to hold it. These Golden Rectangles are gold, so of course, they weigh a lot, but you can see that it conforms to this.

Now, of course, just showing you this and telling you that that's a Golden Rectangle, I haven't actually established that mathematically, that it really is a perfect Golden Rectangle. This construction actually will allow us, though, to establish that, so let me actually verify that the proportions here are, in fact, the Golden Ratio, when we divide. How can we possibly do that?

Well, let's take a look at this. What if I return back to the square? Maybe this is a little tricky to see, but the square is right here. Suppose that square had each side at a length of 2. Okay? That means that this length here is 2, this length here is 2, that's 2, and that's 2. All of these sides are 2, so I'm going to put in 2 here, I'm going to put in 2 here, 2 here, and then this is 2. Remember, though, how I formed that line here? This is actually cutting it in half, so that in fact, this is a 1, and this is a 1.

Now, what I want to do is to find this length right here. I know the length from here to here is 1, and I want to find the length from here to here, to find out what the total length of the base is. Well, that seems like a hard length to figure out, until we realize that it is actually the radius of the circle I made, which actually has this as its radius as well.

Now I can recognize the fact that I have a little right triangle here, and with that right triangle in play, I can use the Pythagorean theorem that Mike alluded to in Lecture Three. In fact, he's going to actually prove it in his next lecture [Lecture 8], so that we're going to see a few proofs of the Pythagorean theorem. But for now, I will just use the Pythagorean theorem to say that this length squared, which is 4, plus this length squared, which is 1, if you add them together, you get 5, and if you take the square root, that gives you the length of this hypotenuse. This is the square root of 5. By the way, familiar number—square root of 5. This length is the square root of 5, and therefore, similarly, this length here is the square root of 5, so that's the square root of 5. Well, if this is the square root of 5, and this is the number 1, then this base has a length of 1 plus the square root of 5. I divide it by the height, which is 2, and look what we have: 1 plus the square root of 5, all divided by 2—the Golden Ratio. Now, we have confirmed that this geometric construction actually results in a perfect Golden Rectangle. A perfect Golden Rectangle.

Now, in fact, this triangle is sort of an important triangle, right? It was sort of key to the picture here; it used the Pythagorean Theorem. It's a 1, 2. This leg is twice as long as that leg. It turns out that that triangle is sometimes referred to as a *Golden Triangle*, and it's sort of neat. I want to show you an example of a Golden Triangle. Here's a bigger example of a Golden Triangle. You can see that the height is actually twice the base. That's sort of interesting. Why would anyone care about this? Well, I wanted to show you one amazing property about the Golden Triangle.

Let's just take a random triangle first. Here's just a random triangle, not particularly interesting, but every triangle has the following amazing property. If you take four copies of it that are smaller, you can always use them to actually produce a larger copy of the original triangle. Here, I have four reduced copies of the triangle, and I can use them to actually produce a bigger version. They are actually all similar to the original one. You can always take a triangle, and cut it up into four pieces, each of which is similar to the original one.

The Golden Triangle, though, has the property that you can do it with five pieces. Now, look at this. This is a stunning example. Notice that each of these triangles here, themselves are perfect Golden Triangles. Why? Because I claim that this is half of this length, and you can see that by looking at this figure, because notice that here, I have that length, and here is another copy of that length, and it perfectly fits with this longer leg. Notice, though, that the way these are configured—I can maybe draw it like this—you see that that configuration produces another, larger version of a perfect right triangle that is actually 2 by 1. It turns out that this is the only triangle that has the feature that you can construct a bigger version of it by using five smaller versions and putting it together.

There is, then, some sort of regeneration process that we are seeing here, and in fact, this is foreshadowing for our next lecture, where we are actually going to see some regeneration features about the Golden Rectangle itself. This is just a little foreshadowing of what we are going to see, in fact, in the next lecture.

Where are we? What we have seen, in fact, are issues of aesthetics, and we've seen mathematical reflections. Now, is the mathematics there? Well, absolutely. What about with the aesthetics? This is actually an open question. Do we really see these rectangles around us, or not? Well, certainly some artists actually put that proportion and those rectangles in their works. Other times, we see reflections of it, but we aren't sure whether it's deliberate or not. In either case, it really brings intrigue, and certainly a tight connection between our aesthetic tastes. It also raises the question: Is it possible that somehow even our aesthetic tastes, what we find appealing, might have some mathematical underpinnings? It's perhaps even a sobering or scary thought to even consider that potential realization, but at least with respect to the Golden Ratio and the Golden Rectangle, we do, in fact, see some connections between aesthetics and mathematics.

I'd like to actually close with one final example, but the example is not one that I can just physically show you, even though it seems peculiar. If we are talking about geometry and the Golden Rectangle, after all, it should be a visual image of some kind: architecture, painting, sculpture.

Well, this is an example that, in fact, has musical underpinnings. Claude Debussy was fascinated with the Golden Rectangle and the Golden Ratio; in fact, he tried to capture that number and those proportions in his musical works. Thus, if we take a look at an example, in particular, if we look at his work, prelude to *The Afternoon of a Faun*, what we see is something fairly surprising.

If you look at this image, this is an image that represents the musical pulses of this work, prelude to *The Afternoon of a Faun*, and it's complicated. These musical pulses are known as *quaver units*, and these are small units of music that you can measure things. I want you to notice that the piece is divided up into various phrases, depending on the fortissimo. You'll notice that at bar 70, for example, there's a real fortissimo right there. If you notice a little bit to the left of that, though, you'll see that there is a fortissimo at bar 19, there's another fortissimo at bar 28, and then another fortissimo at bar 47. If you notice, if you take the 19 and you add the 28, you get bar 47. Thus, we see this Fibonacci pattern occurring in his work—again, very deliberate. If you look at some of the actual original sheet music, you will see the Fibonacci numbers written on the side, and the Golden Ratio there, as he's trying to get the ratios of the music to actually conform.

Now, if you look at the entire piece of music, this piece right here, the one that is being visualized through the quaver units here, we are actually going to listen to this, and if you were to time that, it turns out that the piece we are going to listen to is exactly 129 seconds long, just a little over two minutes.

Now, if you were just to time the beginning of the piece all the way to that major fortissimo at bar 70, the one that's illustrated there, you can see that the piece is building to that. It starts off piano, and then it slowly builds, and builds, and builds, and then it comes up to this thunderous bar 70, and then you see it slowly, gradually comes back down to pianissimo.

If you take the length of time between the beginning of the piece and that huge fortissimo, and you take that and put that into the entire length of the piece of music, then you will see something amazing, and I will tell you what we see. The entire piece of music will last 129 seconds, and the time from the beginning of the piece until that big fortissimo is 81 seconds. If you divide those two things, what is that ratio? It works out to be 1.59259. Look how close it is to the Golden Ratio of 1.61, etc. Very, very deliberate and intentional, and I want you now to sit back and actually listen to the two minutes of this piece of music, and see if you can actually hear the Golden Ratio inside Debussy's prelude to *The Afternoon of a Faun*.

[Music plays.]

Is part of the beauty and elegance of Debussy's work due to the appearance of the Fibonacci pattern and the occurrence of the Golden Ratio in that work? Well, aesthetics and mathematics are deeply related, and there's mathematics in beauty and beauty in mathematics. The Golden Rectangle is one of the most visible shapes to have appeared in the aesthetic and artistic creations throughout the ages. In the next lecture, we will take look at why so many people find that rectangle attractive. We will come back to the Golden Triangle, where we saw a self-regeneration property, and we will see that the Golden Rectangle actually has one as well, which might provide some mathematical underpinnings for why we think the Golden Rectangle is so darn cute. I'll see you there.

Lecture Seven
The Hidden Beauty of the Golden Rectangle

Edward B. Burger, Ph.D.

Scope:

Why the appeal? Why do we see proportions conforming to the Golden Ratio in so many works of art? The architect Le Corbusier overtly included the Golden Rectangle in his designs. Looking at a villa designed by Le Corbusier, we notice that the living area creates a large square, while the open patio has a rectangular shape. When we compare the proportions of the whole villa to those of the small rectangular patio, we discover that both are perfect Golden Rectangles! This rectangular similarity is actually a fundamental and beautiful mathematical property of the Golden Rectangle—one that might illuminate why the Golden Rectangle is so aesthetically pleasing.

Outline

I.   In this lecture, we return to the Golden Rectangle and the Golden Ratio, or the *ratio of the extreme to the mean*.

    A. We will examine the intrinsic properties of the Golden Rectangle that seem to make it so appealing.

    B. We will also learn the power of seeking the essential as a strategy for thinking. In this strategy, we reduce a complex situation to its essential feature to define the situation and make discoveries about it.

II. We begin by reviewing the construction process for a Golden Rectangle.

    A. We started with a perfect square, bisected its base, then drew an arc starting at the midpoint of the base and extending as part of a large circle to a point on the base outside the original square. We connected the extended base and top of the square with a perpendicular line to form a Golden Rectangle.

    B. We proved that the construction was a Golden Rectangle using the Pythagorean theorem.

C. We next return to the villa we saw in the last lecture, deliberately designed by Le Corbusier to include Golden Rectangles.

    1. In the design of the patio in relation to the villa, Le Corbusier captured the same construction process that we went through to build a Golden Rectangle.

    2. Further, if we focus only on the patio of the villa, we see another Golden Rectangle.

    3. In other words, the rectangle we added on to the perfect square with which we began the construction process is, itself, a Golden Rectangle.

    4. Verifying this assertion, we find that the ratio of the base to the height of the smaller rectangle is $\dfrac{2}{\sqrt{5}-1}$, which does not seem to be the same as the Golden Ratio, $\dfrac{1+\sqrt{5}}{2}$. If we use a calculator to compute the ratio, however, we find that the result is $1.618033989....$

    5. Using algebra, we can confirm that the two numbers that result from these ratios are identical.

D. If we remove the largest possible perfect square from our smaller Golden Rectangle, we can repeat the process, leaving yet another Golden Rectangle. Indeed, this regeneration property may provide some insight into why the Golden Rectangle is so aesthetically appealing.

III. We also note that in each square of the sequence of Golden Rectangles, we draw an arc that is one-quarter of a larger circle.

A. If we arrange those arcs in the squares of our succession of Golden Rectangles, we form a natural spiral.

B. This spiral is sometimes called a *logarithmic spiral*. We see it in nature in the Nautilus shell, and it may have served as the inspiration for Matisse's painting *L'Escargot*.

C. Finding the center point of the spiral is relatively easy.

    1. First, we draw a diagonal line from one corner of the largest underlying rectangle to the other. We then draw another diagonal connecting opposite corners on the next largest Golden Rectangle.

2. The point at which those two lines intersect is the center point of the spiral.

3. The spiral itself has other interesting properties that can be analyzed through mathematics.

IV. Mathematics is serious business, of course, but occasionally, it crosses the line into myth and mischief.

  A. The dollar bill is not a Golden Rectangle, but the portion of it that represents its buying power may be a perfect Golden Rectangle.

  B. In his 1946 drawing *Modulor*, Le Corbusier tried to use a Fibonacci pattern to show the proportions of the human form. This drawing prompts us to wonder whether our belly buttons divide our bodies according to the Golden Ratio.

  C. We should keep our minds open to all the possible appearances of the Golden Rectangle, but the real lesson of this lecture is to seek the essential. In this case, the essential feature of the Golden Rectangle is its regeneration property.

Suggested Reading:

Edward B. Burger and Michael Starbird, *The Heart of Mathematics: An invitation to effective thinking*, Key College Publishing, Section 4.3, "The Sexiest Rectangle: Finding aesthetics in life, art, and math through the Golden Rectangle."

Questions to Consider:

1. Consider the diagonal in the Golden Rectangle and suppose we draw in the largest square we can. Notice that one edge of the square cuts the diagonal into two pieces. Verify that the ratio of the length of the entire diagonal to the length of the part of the diagonal that is inside the square is the Golden Ratio.

2. Determine the dimensions of a rectangle such that if you remove the largest square, then what remains has a ratio of base to height that is twice the ratio of base to height of the original rectangle.

Lecture Seven—Transcript
The Hidden Beauty of the Golden Rectangle

Well, in these past lectures we have been exploring and enjoying the Golden Ratio and the Golden Rectangle, the rectangle that captures the essence and the spirit of the Golden Ratio because of it's proportions; if you take the length of the base and divide it by the length of the height, you get the perfect number, the Golden Ratio, which is 1 plus the square root of 5, all divided by 2, which, again, has the decimal you probably have memorized, 1.618033 and so on.

Well, sometimes this Golden Ratio is referred to as the *ratio of the extreme to the mean*. That's sometimes another way of saying the Golden Ratio. In fact, Johannes Kepler once noted that: "Geometry has two great treasures: one is the Theorem of Pythagoras; the other the division of a line into extreme and mean ratio. The first we may compare to a measure of gold; the second we may name a precious jewel."

Well, in this lecture, I want us to once again return to the extreme and mean ratio, or the Golden Ratio. Actually, in the next lecture, Mike will pick up the action into geometry, and take a look at the other treasure, namely, the Pythagorean theorem.

The point of this lecture is severalfold. First of all, the mathematical underpinnings really involved trying to answer the following question: Are there some intrinsic properties about the Golden Rectangle that make it so interesting, so appealing, to humanity throughout the ages? Perhaps more importantly though is the thinking lesson. Remember, this is a course on the joy of thinking, and really, this lecture, and our quest to try to see hidden structure, hidden within the Golden Rectangle, is going to be a powerful and wonderful example of the power of seeking the essential. By taking a complicated issue, whittling it down, and finding that essential feature that really classifies it as the object, the critical feature, that quest for seeking the essential is so valuable and important, and often leads to incredible discoveries.

Right now, what I want to do is examine and explore that possible way of thinking through the quest for a potential rationale for why we find this particular rectangle so appealing. The way I would like to begin is to first just review how we build a Golden Rectangle. Let's just remind ourselves how you can actually construct one.

Here's the construction that we did in the previous lecture, where we actually demonstrated a way of producing one.

Let me just remind you how this works. We started originally with this perfect square, which here is marked by a 2-by-2 square. We then cut the bottom length in half, so that each one of these is a 1, and then I took a compass, and I drew an arc whose center is actually here at this midpoint, and the radius is actually this length, and then I drew that arc down, so that this is actually part of a very large circle. I saw where that arc of the circle actually intersected the extended base, if you would allow me to extend the base until I have that point of intersection, I then extended the top of the square correspondingly. Then I drew a perpendicular line that went right from the point of intersection of the arc of the circle and the floor, up right to the ceiling. And this outer rectangle, in fact, is a perfect Golden Rectangle.

In fact, we proved it by looking at this math here. For example, I remind you that we discovered that this is a right triangle, in fact a Golden Triangle, where this has length 2, and this has length 1, using the Pythagorean theorem that Mike will prove up next. What we see is that 2^2 plus 1^2, which is 5, will equal the length of this, once we take the square root of 5. This is actually a radius of this very large circle, but this, too, represents the radius of that same circle, so that since this length is the square root of 5, this length is also the square root of 5, so we have the square root of 5 here, and this addition of 1 here, so that the entire base has length 1 plus the square root of 5, and if we divide that by the height, which I remind you is 2, you see the perfect Golden Ratio: 1 plus the square root of 5, over 2. This really is, in fact, a perfect Golden Rectangle, and that's the construction.

I also want us to think about the Golden Rectangle in another example that we saw in our architecture, in the French villa designed by Le Corbusier. The image that you're seeing right now is, in fact, of that French villa. Remember that if we put a large rectangle around the villa, including the top most parts of the chimney and the roof, what you see, in fact, is a perfect Golden Rectangle. As we mentioned in the previous lecture, that is, in fact, extremely deliberate. This was not coincidental. It is, in fact, exact and deliberate, since Le Corbusier actually perceived mathematics to be soothing to the human spirit, and he actually tried to embrace mathematical ideas and incorporate them into the surroundings, in this case, the villa.

Now, if you look at the villa or return to this image, you'll see something interesting. Remember that in our construction, we started with a square, and then we added on some stuff, almost like a little addition, if you will, to make a beautiful, perfect Golden Rectangle. Let's take a look at Le Corbusier's villa one more time. If we look at the villa, we see something sort of interesting. If you look at it, what you see is that on the right portion is the villa, and in that left area, we see, in fact, that outdoor patio region. If we were to draw line where the actual interior of the villa resides, so that we draw a vertical line down, to separate the interior portion of the villa from the exterior patio, you'll notice that the interior portion of the villa is, in fact, a perfect square. In fact, then, Le Corbusier has actually done a little bit more. He has actually captured this construction. Do you see it? The square is the interior portion of the villa, and then this rectangular portion here, you see, is in fact the patio, so that he has actually even captured the construction, which is quite fascinating.

Now, let's actually take a look at that patio, or correspondingly, at this rectangle right here, and in fact, on the image that you're going to look at, what I did was to just take the patio, put it on its side, and enlarged to be the same size as the original villa, so that I just increased the magnification of that picture. Now, I want you look at that rectangle, and I'm going to ask you to see if you are drawn to it, or, in this image, I want you look at this rectangle, the little rectangle that we had to add on to the square to make the totality a perfect Golden Rectangle.

In particular—maybe this is a little bit funny to do—I am actually going to put this on its side, but now I just want you to focus on this. Just focus on this. What do you think about that rectangle? Do you like it? Do you like it? Well, in fact, this, I claim, is another perfect Golden Rectangle. In order to make a perfect Golden Rectangle, then, we take a square, we do this construction, and we add on a rectangle to make a totality of a huge Golden Rectangle, but the rectangle that we had to add on, I claim, is another perfect Golden Rectangle, or, in the image of the villa by Le Corbusier, if you look at the patio portion and put the patio on its side, what do we have? We have another perfect Golden Rectangle.

Now, first of all, let's just ask ourselves: Why is that true? Well, let's just verify it. Here we go. Let's look at the image that we have here. We are going to look at this rectangle, and I'm going to want to look at base divided by height, and see, if, in fact, it has the right ratio. Now remember though, this rectangle is sort of on its side. We think of the rectangle, really, as being like this, so that the base here is going to be this, and the height will be this.

Well, what's the base? I'm going to turn it back again. The base, which is currently this length, is 2, so I am going to come back here, and just write "2" here. The height of this rectangle—well, let's turn it back one more time and see what that is. Well, that actually corresponds to this length right here. What is that length right here? That might seem like a difficult length to compute. Maybe we need some sort of highbrow mathematics, but not at all, because I remind you that this entire length here is actually the square root of 5, and we know this length to be 1, so this length is easy to compute. It is just the square root of 5 once I subtract the 1, so that, in fact, this length is just the square root of 5 minus 1.

If I turn this back for one last time, what I see here is that this length is the square root of 5 minus the number 1, $\sqrt{5} - 1$. Therefore, what is the ratio of base to height? That's going to be 2 divided by the number square root of 5 minus 1, $\dfrac{2}{\sqrt{5} - 1}$.

Well, wait a minute, 2 divided by the square root of 5 minus 1 does not, to me, sound like the Golden Ratio. It does not sound like "1 plus the square root of 5, divided by 2." This, then, does not sound good, but here's a great experiment that I invite all of you to try. Plug this number into a calculator. That is, let's take 2 and divide it by the quantity square root of 5 minus 1. If you actually want to try this, by the way, the way I suggest you do it, unless you have a very fancy calculator, is to first compute the square root of 5, then subtract the number 1, then store that number in memory or something, or write it down, and then take 2 and divide it by that number, and push the equals sign. You know what you get? It turns out that you get 1.618033989 and so on. It corresponds perfectly to the decimal expansion for the Golden Ratio.

Wait a minute, though. This does not look like the Golden Ratio of 1 plus the square root of 5, divided by 2, $\dfrac{1+\sqrt{5}}{2}$. This is 2 divided by the square root of 5 minus 1, $\dfrac{2}{\sqrt{5}-1}$. Well, it turns out that with just a little bit of algebra, you can actually confirm that not just the decimals agree up to a certain point, but, in fact, the two numbers are identical.

Just for fun, I thought I would just do, literally, under one minute's worth of arithmetic algebra for you. You can just sit back and enjoy it if you want to, or let it sort of wash over you, but I thought it would be fun to really confirm for sure that this is indeed a perfect Golden Rectangle, not just because the decimals line up for a while, but because they are exact.

Now, the trick is to take this number—2 divided by the square root of 5 minus 1—and do something to it in order to make it look like 1 plus the square root of 5, divided by 2. Here's the amazing trick: It turns out that in mathematics, and in arithmetic in particular, when a question is really tricky, a great method for resolving it is to multiply the number by 1. If you multiply the number by 1, nothing changes, because 1 has that wonderful property that 1 times anything is the anything. I can elect to write 1, though, in a very exotic way. In particular, I could write it as 5 divided by 5, because 5 divided by 5 is just 1, after all, or 17 divided by 17, since that's just, after you cancel, 1.

The number I'm actually going to multiply 2 divided by the square root of 5 minus 1 by, is going to be something divided by itself, so that it's just multiplying by 1, but it's going to be a very interesting one. It's going to be precisely the thing we want to look at: 1 plus the square root of 5, divided by 1 plus the square root of 5. That's something divided by itself, so it just cancels, and it's 1.

What happens when you do the multiplication, though? Well, on the top, we have 2 times that quantity, 1 plus the square root of 5. On the bottom, we have this really awful-looking thing that perhaps gives so many people nightmares about their algebra experiences in school. We see the quantity square root of 5 minus 1, times the quantity 1 plus the square root of 5, $\left(\sqrt{5}-1\right)\times\left(1+\sqrt{5}\right)$. Well, if you actually multiply that all out using a little bit of algebra that we learned and forgot a long time ago, it turns out that that denominator works out to be the number 4. We then have 2 times the number 1 plus the square root of 5, but I'm dividing by 4, so that the 2 on the top and the 4 on the bottom actually cancel, and I'm left with a 2 on the bottom, or, 1 plus the square root of 5, divided by 2. We get the Golden Ratio. In fact, then, this is a perfect Golden Rectangle.

Anyway, that's a little bit of algebra that confirms it, but in any case, you could try it on a calculator and convince yourself that, in fact, we are right on target.

Well, okay, but this is fantastic, because if this is a Golden Rectangle, then, if I cut off the largest possible square that I can, I'm left with a little rectangle here, and what about that rectangle? Well, it's a Golden Rectangle by the exact same principle. I start with a big Golden Rectangle, cut off the biggest square, and I'm left with a Golden Rectangle. Repeat: Cut off the biggest square, and I'm left with another Golden Rectangle. I can actually repeat this again. Cut off the biggest square, and I'm left with a Golden Rectangle.

If I were to do that, what we would get is a fantastic image that would look like this. I cut off this square, I get a Golden Rectangle. I cut off this square from the Golden Rectangle, and I get another Golden Rectangle. I cut off this square, and I get another Golden Rectangle, and I can keep doing this.

Now, the really neat thing is that this regeneration property might actually provide an insight into why this rectangle is so aesthetically appealing to us. It has this regeneration feature, and in fact, this is the only rectangle we can draw that has this property, that if you cut off the square, what you are left with, in fact, is similar to the entire original whole. This might explain, then, why we are drawn to it somehow. There is no other rectangle that in fact has this property. This might actually be a potential mathematical explanation, then, for why people have been drawn to it throughout humanity.

Now, armed with this, you may remember that we had these circle arcs. If this, in fact, is a square, I could actually draw, if I wanted to, an enormous quarter of a circle. Since this is a square, I can actually put it in the quarter of a circle, and let me just do that for you. You can see that it is, of course, a perfect square that this quarter of a circle fits perfectly in, but now, this is a square, and I can put a quarter circle inside of it, much smaller, of course.

Now, this is a square, so I can put a quarter circle inside of it. Well, this is a square, so I can put a little, teeny quarter circle in there. And this is a square, so I can put a little quarter circle in here. And here's a square, so I can put a little quarter circle in here. You can keep repeating this process if you want to. What you generate is a really beautiful spiral, so that the spiral curve is sort of a spectacular curve that is naturally coming out. Sometimes this is referred to as the *logarithmic spiral.* In fact, my producer generated a beautiful picture of this that I would like to share with you. You can really see that spiral just spiraling in in quite a spectacular fashion.

In fact, by the way, this has been the inspiration for many things. First of all, in the art world, we have seen reflections of this. In fact, it is said that this particular curve was Matisse's inspiration for his work *L'Escargot*, and if you see that beautiful collage of colors, he's trying to capture the beauty of the spiral. In fact, then, art is inspired by this mathematical object, but so is nature, long before Matisse. In fact, if you've ever taken a look at the Nautilus shell, you see a curve of this kind, and it even becomes more intriguing when you cut it in half and you compare. It really is beautiful to see how closely nature conforms with the mathematics that we're discovering, all from the Golden Ratio, all from the Golden Rectangle. There are some beautiful reflections, then, in this object.

Actually, though, let's take a look at this spiral. And sadly, I'm going to deface this beautiful image to make an interesting point, for this spiral seems to be spiraling around to some center point. There is some center point to that spiral, and I actually want to show you how easy it is to find that center point.

It seems like it might be really difficult, but in fact it's not. All I'm going to do is to connect this corner to this corner. I'm going to draw in this diagonal. I'm going to do this live, and I really feel sort of guilty about defacing this picture. Maybe I should put a plastic transparency over it so that we could have the picture to celebrate later, but maybe this will even make the picture more beautiful. Of course, you will be the final judge. Of course, beauty is in the eye of the beholder.

I just drew the diagonal, then, of this large Golden Rectangle here, but now, this is a Golden Rectangle right here, and I'm just going to draw the diagonal so that it goes from here up to here. I'm just going to draw two diagonals, one for the large Golden Rectangle, and then one for the next largest one after the largest one. You notice that those two diagonals intersect. The point of intersection is very clear, and it turns out that that is the precise point where the spiral is going to spiral around infinitely, as many times as you keep repeating this. That, in fact, is the center of the spiral, the point where the spiral just keeps spinning, spinning, spinning around as you go deeper and deeper into it.

Then, even these lines have amazing properties. For example, suppose you take this entire line, and look at this piece, and compare it to this piece. It turns out that the ratio is the Golden Ratio. Golden Ratios, then, abound in the Golden Rectangle, not just in the base and the height, but, in fact, in many, many, many properties of it, even in the location of the spiral for this logarithmic curve.

Now, this center point, by the way, has some very interesting properties. Let me just try to make that center point much clearer so that everyone can see it with the big blue dot. Let me show you a really neat fact about this logarithmic spiral that you might get a kick out of. In fact, this spiral, which was made by all of these different quarters of circles, comes together in a collective whole in a very intriguing way. Pick any point that you want along this core point, for example, pick a point right here. Pick any point along that spiral, and now, draw a line that just grazes that point right there.

Now, take that point of tangency, and connect it to the very center point of the spiral. If you do that, what you see in this case is—if I do like this, I have to be a little bit careful, so that we get this back up, so it just touches there, let's say, and I connect it to the center point—you will notice that an angle is formed by these two black lines. There are two angles, in fact, but you can look at either one of them, and you'll see that there is an angle.

It turns out that no matter where on the spiral you pick a point, those angles will be the same as these angles. For example, those two angles will actually be the same as if I picked a point way over here, looked at the point of tangency, and drew a line from the center of the spiral to there. Those two angles are the same as the other two angles that we just saw.

Similarly, if I pick this point, say, right here—I will be a little bit less brave—just a point of tangency, and connect them, those angles are, in fact, the same as the original two angles we saw. All the angles are the same, so that somehow, this center point and this curve come together beautifully to actually create an image that is somehow not only captured by nature, but, in fact, can be understood and analyzed through mathematics. Anyway, I think that's just a beautiful image to reflect and to enjoy, and also to see reflections of it in nature.

Okay, well, certainly we all know that mathematics is serious business, and certainly, a hard science, but sometimes it can also cross the line into mathematical myth, and even mischief. I wanted to illustrate some of these issues with some silly examples. You see, some people actually see great things in their tealeaves and so forth, and other people actually see reflections of the Golden Rectangle everywhere. Well, not every rectangle is a Golden Rectangle, and sometimes we see it not necessarily where it really is, but we think we see it. Let me give you some examples.

Here is an example. Take a look at the dollar bill. Now, on top here I put a perfect Golden Rectangle. I built a perfect Golden Rectangle; you can see that it is actually gold, and then on the bottom here is an U.S. $1 bill. Do you think that this rectangle, in fact, has the same proportions as the Golden Rectangle?

Well, probably not, because this looks way too long. It looks way too long. It should be shorter, so the answer is "no." This is an example of a rectangle that is not a Golden Rectangle. However, as a little footnote, if you consider the buying power of the dollar, actually, it is a perfect Golden Rectangle. Well, okay, that's sort of a joke I made up, but certainly, it does illustrate the point that you can see the Golden Rectangle here, and it illustrates the point that sometimes, really, the Golden Rectangle might not be there even though we would like to be.

Another wonderful example of this in the art world is Le Corbusier's wonderful ink drawing from 1946 called *Modulor*, where he tried to take the body, the human figure, and partition it with Fibonacci-type patterns in order to capture proportions that conform to the Golden Ratio. For example, if you look at that figure, this is the image that he drew. You'll see numbers that he put there. These are the numbers that he put there. This is, in fact, the original image.

If you look on the very, very bottom, though, in that first column, the left-hand column, and you read from the bottom up, you will see that he marked things like the height of the toe, and the height of the foot, and the ankle, and so forth, and look at those numbers. I don't know if you can read them, but I will read them to you. The very bottom-most one is a six. The one above it is a nine. The one above it is a 15, and notice that 6 plus 9 is 15.

The next number up is 24, which you will notice is, in fact, 9 plus 15. Then, above the 24 is the 39, and so forth. The pattern continues. This, in fact, is an example of a recurrent sequence with different starting seeds, but the same generating process. In fact, we know, then, that the ratios will, in fact, conform to the Golden Ratio. Thus, again, very deliberate.

You also notice that the bellybutton there is marked; you can see that in the center of the figure, and in fact, this brings up a funny myth, which is that if you actually were to measure the height from your feet up to your bellybutton, and then the height from your bellybutton up to the top of your head, and looked at that ratio, it should be a Golden Ratio if you are the ideal proportions. Well, in the privacy your own home, you can see how close you come to the ideal, if you believe this, and certainly, this is not at all scientifically or mathematically proven, but certainly, it is reflected in Le Corbusier's work.

Do we, then, see the Golden Rectangle, or not? Certainly, we have seen many examples in the past two lectures, where artists and mathematicians have actually incorporated this figure and these proportions, and the Fibonacci pattern, certainly deliberately, in their works. We see it in other places, and we just don't know the answer. It remains an open question as to whether or not we see reflections of these things and whether they really are there, or we're seeing something that comes close to them. I think the truth is that we should certainly keep an open mind as we examine these issues, issue by issue.

However, the real life lesson here that I want us all to embrace is the idea of seeking the essential. In the case of the Golden Rectangle, what we saw was the essential feature of the Golden Rectangle, which was that it had this regeneration property. If you were to cut off the largest square you possibly could, the remaining smaller rectangle, is, in fact, another example of a Golden Rectangle, and you can repeat that process. That essential feature, which only the Golden Rectangle possesses, might, in fact, be an explanation for why this is so appealing.

Well, I thought I would try one last frivolous example with you, if you will indulge me. It is something that I have actually never tried, so this is actually a first, but just as the bellybutton saga, where if you measure the proportion from your feet to your bellybutton, and your bellybutton to your head, it is supposed to give you, in the ideal setting, the Golden Ratio, it is also said that if you look at the dimensions of the palm of your hand, that in fact, that should conform to the Golden Rectangle.

Well, here I drew a rough sketch of a perfect Golden Rectangle as best I could, late last night, and I'm going to try this right now live. I actually have an ink pad here, and I'm going to now—and I've never done this, and I will report that in fact, it is very sticky, but I'm doing this live, just for you. I really hope you understand. Now, we're going to try this, and see what happens, so that you can see that I am covered with ink, and now, I am going to try to put it down here. You know, you only get one shot. You can't just put it put it down, and lift it up, and try again. This is a onetime deal, it's live, and here we are in class, and I'm doing it right now. I'm going to make an imprint, and I am going to lift it up.

Well, there you have it. It certainly does not look like my hand conforms to the Golden Rectangle. My middle finger, there, is sticking out way too much, although the top and the bottom fit in pretty nicely, but still, it doesn't look that way. Maybe my hand does not have some sort of Platonic aesthetic ideal proportion. Well, whether or not it's an exact fit, through this life lesson of seeking the essential, we really do, indeed, have the beautiful Golden Rectangle in the palms of our hands.

In the next lecture, we will consider further issues in classical geometry, as Mike takes us through various realms, including lots of proofs of the Pythagorean theorem, which has so fruitfully served us so well.

Lecture Eight
The Pythagorean Theorem and Geometry of Ellipses

Michael Starbird, Ph.D.

Scope:

If we had to select only one theorem as the best representative of all of mathematics, we might well choose the Pythagorean theorem. This theorem was proved in about 500 B.C. or before and captures an essential relationship among the sides of a right triangle. Now, dozens of proofs of this theorem are known, and in this lecture, we will see several extremely elegant ones.

The ancient Greek school of mathematics developed the study of geometry. Among the constructs of classical geometry, the conic sections stand out for their attractive forms and for their descriptions in terms of the locus of points satisfying a condition. Here, we will present a beautiful description that shows that the cut-cone description of the ellipse yields a set of points for which the sum of the distances to two fixed points is a constant.

Outline

I. The Pythagorean theorem is the best-known theorem in mathematics. It states that in a right triangle, the square of the hypotenuse is equal to the sum of the squares of the other two sides.

   A. The history of the theorem dates back at least to 1600 B.C. in Babylonia. It easily shatters the boundaries of time.

   B. Its name is associated with the Greek Pythagorean school, which was founded in about 540 B.C.

   1. The school had a strict code of secrecy.

   2. The Pythagoreans were also vegetarians who were not allowed to eat beans.

II. Bhaskara's proof of the Pythagorean theorem, dating from 12th-century India, may win the award as most elegant.

   A. We take four copies of our right triangle, together with a small square, and construct a square on the hypotenuse.

   1. The total area of those five pieces is equal to the square on the hypotenuse.

2. By moving two of the triangles, the pieces can be reassembled to construct two smaller squares, each of which is a square of a leg of the right triangle.

3. The area remains constant because the same pieces are used; we see, then, that the square on the hypotenuse is equal to the sum of the squares of the other two sides.

4. Bhaskara's proof is a geometric demonstration of the Pythagorean theorem.

B. Another extremely elegant proof of the Pythagorean theorem involves the same four copies of the right triangle.

1. We begin by placing our four copies of the right triangle inside a square frame. The total area of the outer square is the sum of the sides of the four triangles plus the square of the hypotenuse.

2. Rearranging the pieces shows that the area outside the four triangles is also equal to the sum of the two smaller squares, with sides equal to the lengths of the other two legs of the right triangle.

C. President Garfield has a proof of the Pythagorean theorem attributed to him.

1. We arrange two copies of the right triangle to complete a trapezoid by joining the two free vertices, the short side plus the long side $(a+b)$. In other words, the height of the trapezoid is the short side plus the long side $(a+b)$; the bottom is b and the top is a.

2. The area of a trapezoid is the height times half the sum of the bases.

3. We would write the equation as $$\frac{(a+b)(a+b)}{2} = \frac{\left(a^2+2ab+b^2\right)}{2}.$$

4. The total area is also equal to the sum of the areas of the three triangles in the picture, namely, $\dfrac{ab}{2}$, $\dfrac{ab}{2}$, and $\dfrac{c^2}{2}$ (c is the hypotenuse).

5. Setting these two views of the area as equal and simplifying gives the result:

$$\frac{a^2 + 2ab + b^2}{2} = \frac{2ab + c^2}{2}$$

$$a^2 + b^2 = c^2$$

III. Conic sections are geometric shapes that have two quite different types of descriptions.

  A. Consider a right circular cone and look at the intersections that arise when we cut it with a plane.

   1. If we cut it horizontally, of course, we get a circle.

   2. If we cut it at an angle, we get an oval-shaped curve called an *ellipse*.

   3. If we cut it parallel to a line on the cone, we get a *parabola*.

   4. If we cut it at a steeper angle, we hit both branches of the cone and get a two-part curve, the *hyperbola*.

  B. These same curves can be described in an entirely different way as a so-called *locus of points*.

   1. The circle is the set of points in the plane equidistant from a fixed point, its center. Alternatively, this same idea is phrased in the statement that the circle is the locus of points equidistant from a fixed point. Taking a string, pinning one end on a table, and tracing with a pencil what the other end traverses as we move it around the fixed point draws a circle.

   2. The ellipse is the set of points in the plane such that the sum of the distances to two fixed points, the *foci*, is a constant. Fixing two pins on a table, encircling them with a loose loop, pulling the loop taut, and moving it around the pins draws an ellipse. The string illustrates the idea that the sum of the distances to the two fixed points is a constant.

  C. We have two quite different descriptions for these curves. Let's consider the ellipse and see why the two descriptions both fit that curve.

   1. Remember that if we cut a cone at an angle with a plane, the resulting shape is an ellipse.

2. A different description of an ellipse is that it is the set of points in a plane such that the sum of the distances to two fixed points is a constant.

3. Imagine that we place two balls in the cone, like scoops of ice cream, one above the plane that is cutting through the cone and one below the plane. We make these balls the exact size so that they fit snugly in the cone and are tangent to the plane.

4. The amazing fact is that the two points of tangency are the foci, the fixed points, of the ellipse. In mathematics, amazing facts are the result of reason; we can expect to find an explanation for this one, and we do.

5. As a preliminary observation, if we look at a sphere, we see that the distances from an external point to any two tangent points are the same.

6. Similarly, if we use a circle, we can confirm what we observed with the sphere. The distances from an external point to any two tangent points are the same.

7. Returning to the ellipse, we examine a simpler case of the same shapes in the plane.

8. We see that the distance between tangent points on one side of the flat V-shape is the same as the distance between tangent points on the other side.

9. The distance from a point on the ellipse to a focus equals the distance on the cone up or down to the place that the ball nestles in the cone.

10. The sum of the distances to the two foci is equal to the constant distance between the two nestling circles of the two balls.

11. This proves that the intersection of a plane with a right circular cone does give an ellipse.

D. This proof shows us the value of simplifying a complicated situation to illustrate the fundamental reasons that a certain assertion is true.

Suggested Reading:

Edward B. Burger and Michael Starbird, *The Heart of Mathematics: An invitation to effective thinking*, Key College Publishing, Section 4.1, "Pythagoras and His Hypotenuse: How a puzzle leads to the proof of one of the gems of mathematics."

Questions to Consider:

1. Train tracks are made of metal. Consequently, they expand when it's warm and shrink when it's cold. When riding in a train, you hear the clickety-clack of the wheels going over small gaps left in the tracks to allow for this expansion. Suppose you were a beginner at laying railroad tracks and forgot to put in the gaps. Instead you made a track one mile long that was firmly fixed at each end. On a hot day, suppose the track expanded by two feet and therefore buckled up in the middle creating a triangle. Roughly how high would the mid-point be? Now you may appreciate the click-clack of the railroad track.

2. If the lines on a cone going to the tip of the cone point are extended through the cone point, we get two cones tip to tip. Suppose we take a plane that cuts through both of these cones. Then the intersection of that plane with the cones has two pieces, which are the two branches of that intersection, which is a hyperbola. A hyperbola is the set of all points such that the difference of the distances to two fixed points, the foci, is a constant. Can you guess how to use spheres inside the cones again to find the locations of those two foci?

Lecture Eight—Transcript
The Pythagorean Theorem and Geometry of Ellipses

In Ed's preceding two lectures about the Golden Rectangle, we saw examples of the beauty of pleasing proportion and the interrelationship between mathematics and aesthetics. Of course, the rectangle is just one of the shapes we dream about when we close our eyes on a starry night and think of geometrical beauty. We also dream of triangles—and maybe other shapes as well. In fact, our physical world presents us with all sorts of shapes and forms that give rise to the mathematical world of geometry. This lecture will continue our exploration of the visual world of classical geometry.

In this lecture, we're going to be talking about some really beautiful mathematics, some of the most elegant mathematics that describe the beauty of geometry. And in that, we will not only see these extremely elegant proofs of theorems that were known to the ancient Greeks, but we will also be giving some examples of some methods of inquiry and discovery that I think can be applied in all sorts of arenas of life, not just mathematical ones.

One particular one is to look for the essence of things. Why is something true? What is the essential feature that makes a property true? We will see some examples of that in this lecture.

The second method of investigating the world is to take a complicated situation and decide, "No, that's too complicated to work on. Instead, I will first investigate a simple reflection of it, a simple case, a simpler example that is not quite the whole picture, but will train us." We will train ourselves; we will pick ourselves up by our bootstraps, so that we learn enough to then apply it to the more complicated situation.

Well, the great thing about what we are going to do today is that we are going to start with a theorem that has one of the longest histories of all theorems in mathematics. In fact, if you were to choose one theorem to represent all of mathematics, I think you would probably choose the Pythagorean theorem.

The Pythagorean theorem says that if you have a right triangle such as this one, the square of the hypotenuse is equal to the sum of the squares on the other two sides. Most of you have heard of the Pythagorean theorem. Everyone has probably heard of the

Pythagorean theorem, but I'll bet most of you don't know how to actually prove that that is true.

Well, one of the things about the Pythagorean theorem that makes it so attractive to me is that it shows that mathematics is timeless, and completely universal and global. People have been thinking about the relationship to the Pythagorean theorem from at least 1600 B.C. to the present time. It just easily shatters the bounds of time. That's a wonderful feature of mathematics, and in particular, of this particular theorem.

We saw in Lecture Three that the Babylonians had given examples of right triangles that had whole number sides, as in a 5, 4, 3 triangle. That was an example from ancient Babylonian times, and these examples were found on clay tablets in, remember, 1600 B.C.E.

The Pythagorean theorem is named after Pythagoras, and Pythagoras started a society in ancient Greece, in 540 B.C. It was an interesting society. I wanted to say a couple of things about the Pythagorean society. It had a very strict code of conduct, and one of its features was secrecy. Its members would discover these mathematical insights, and then not tell anybody. They were kept secret. I fear that that concept of keeping mathematics secret from the population has endured to this day. I sometimes fear that we mathematicians don't actually divulge the inner essence of mathematics, but I am hoping to break that pattern today.

The Pythagorean society actually had three tenets. One of them, at least, was secrecy, as I said. Another was that they were vegetarians; no meat. The third one was a curious one that said that they were not allowed to eat beans. Now, I would be happy to go along with this, because I don't like beans, so I think I will join in their society, in that particular aspect.

Pythagoras knew a proof of this theorem back in 500 B.C., but the proof I'm going to show you right now was actually invented in India by a mathematician named Bhaskara, in the 12th century A.D. This is showing the global universality of this concept.

Well, Bhaskara was a wonderful mathematician, and I wanted to tell you one story about him before I give his beautiful proof. The story goes that he had a daughter who was going to be married, and since he was a mathematician—back in those days, there was a lot of overlap in these subjects—he was also an astrologer. He had therefore predicted the perfect time for his daughter to be married. Well, they had a water clock that was measuring the time. His daughter had leaned over the water clock, and a pearl from her necklace fell into the water clock, and blocked the water in the water clock from going out. Because it blocked the water, the time was stopped, and they missed the propitious moment for her wedding.

Bhaskara did not allow his daughter to be married, and I don't know whether she was happy about that or not, but in any case, she wasn't married. He did, however, write a book of mathematics that bears her name, and so, she has lived through history by this tribute to her lack of marital status. Anyway, that's the story of Bhaskara. I will now show you his wonderful proof of the Pythagorean theorem.

The Pythagorean theorem says that the square on the hypotenuse is equal to the sum of the squares of the other two sides. Bhaskara said, "Well, if you are going to talk about the square on the hypotenuse, let's make a square out of whose sides are the hypotenuse." In order to do that, we need four different copies, identical copies, of our right triangle. We have four copies here; one, two, three, four. And he arranged them so that they formed a square. Here we go. We just arranged them so that the hypotenuses are all facing outward. Here they are. See, this hypotenuse pass to face outward. You arrange them into a square, like this. They fit very neatly, four of them. Then, you need a little square in the middle to fill it out.

This, then, is a square on the hypotenuse. Now, look what happens if I just rotate two of these triangles. I'll rotate this one, and I'll rotate this one, and now, the same amount of area has constructed this figure. Look what happens, though, if we put this little marker right here. You can see that this is equal to a square on the shorter side of the right triangle, plus a square on the longer side. He geometrically showed that the square on hypotenuse is the sum of the squares on the other two sides. That's an amazingly beautiful proof of the Pythagorean theorem. We didn't need to write down a single equation, or anything else, to prove it.

Let me just show you another extremely elegant proof. It uses the same four copies of the right triangle. Here's another proof. We just arrange the four copies of the right triangle we're working with into a little square, and notice that if you arrange them in this fashion, the inner part is the square on the hypotenuse. In other words, the total area of this bigger square is the sum of the four copies of the right triangle, plus the square on the hypotenuse.

Let's just rearrange these. Once again, we will just rearrange these triangles. Rearranging them in this fashion, we see that the missing area is now the square on the short side plus the square on the big side. That's another proof of the Pythagorean theorem.

Aren't these great? These are just wonderful proofs. Finally, though, I wanted to show you that one of the presidents of the United States actually contributed to the Pythagorean theorem. President Garfield has his own proof of the Pythagorean theorem, which I will now show you. This is President James Garfield. What he did was to just use two copies of the right triangle, and then he completed this trapezoid. You see? There's a trapezoid. This side is the short side plus the long side—we could call them $(a+b)$—in height. This side is b. The top is a, and the equation of the area of a trapezoid is the height, $(a+b)$, times the average of the base and the top, so that it's $(a+b)$ times $(a+b)$, over 2; $\dfrac{(a+b)(a+b)}{2}$.

That would give the area of the entire trapezoid, but this trapezoid is equal to the area of this piece, which is a times b, over 2, $\dfrac{ab}{2}$ (base times height over 2 is the area of a triangle) plus the area of this piece, a times b, over 2, $\dfrac{ab}{2}$, plus the area of this piece. Well, look. This is a right triangle whose height is c, the hypotenuse, so that the area of this triangle here is the hypotenuse, c, times c over 2, $\dfrac{c^2}{2}$. If you just write the equation that the area of the trapezoid is a plus b over 2 times a plus b, and you set that equal to the sum of these three areas, and just do a little algebra, which you will see on the screen, you'll see that you will conclude that c^2 is equal to a^2 plus b^2. That's James Garfield's proof of the Pythagorean theorem.

I think all of those are wonderfully elegant demonstrations of the truth of that relationship between the sides of a right triangle, but now I want to move on to a three-dimensional concept, and that is the concept of the conic sections. This is a geometric idea that is an elegant way to create beautiful shapes.

This is a cone, like an ice cream cone, and if you take this cone, and you pass a plane through the cone in various ways, you get various curves. If you pass it just straight across this way, as in where this line is, you just get a round circle. If you pass through at sort of a diagonal line, you would get a shape like this. You can see how that shape is. You can see that it is an oval kind of shape, and in fact it is what is called an *ellipse*. The rest of the lecture is going to be about that shape, which is a wonderful shape. This is an ellipse.

If we cut the same cone with a plane that is just parallel to one of the lines on the side of the cone, we get a *parabola*. If you cut even more steeply so that you hit it like this, you get a *hyperbola*. So, there are four conic sections. We are going to be concentrating on just on the ellipse today.

I have given you a description of the conic sections by saying that if you take a cone and cut it, you get this shape. There are other descriptions, though, of those same curves, and I wanted to first show you them, and then talk about the relationship between those two different versions. Here we go.

The first thing is that if we took this cone, and we cut it with a horizontal line, we've got a circle. One description of a circle is that it is the set of all the points that are some fixed distance from a given point. Right? That's what a circle is. This is very simple. I'm just going to draw you a circle, and a good way to draw a circle is to just take a point, take a loop of string, and then just draw it, and you've drawn a perfect circle.

A circle, then, is the set of all the points that are equidistant from a given point in the plane. By the way, I think that came out very well. I'm always surprised when these things work. This is a beautiful example of a circle, then.

Now, I am going to show you another figure that is an ellipse. For an ellipse, we take two pins, two points, and an ellipse is the set of points so that the sum of the distances to two different fixed points is a constant. The sum of the distances to two different points is a constant.

In order to physically draw that, we will take a string, and loop it around both of the pins, and then, notice something about this. If I hold this string in a given place, the distance from this point, my finger, here, to this pin, plus the distance to this pin, is the same as if

I had moved to any other point, like here. You see? The sum is the same, because the total length of the string is constant. It's a loop that has a constant length.

The amount of string between these two pins is constant. That stays fixed. The remaining length of the string, then, is the sum of this length plus this length, no matter where I hold it. If I hold here, this length plus this length is the same as if I were to hold it here, with this length plus this length. You see? This little string is allowing me to produce the set of all the points so that the sum of the distances between two fixed points is constant. Now, I can do this by just marking it—this one is more tricky. It's not only an elegant ellipse, which is really nice, but it has made this beautiful artwork, here, because of the string and the ink that got spilled on it, so that it is a doubly attractive ellipse. This is a wonderful example of an ellipse.

What I want you to focus on—and this is what mathematicians love to think about, and I think that it is an example of looking for connections; looking for connections is what makes mathematics beautiful, and I think, is what makes life beautiful, when you see unexpected convergence of ideas. In this case, there are two ideas that I have told you about, and you have to keep them separate, because they're totally separate ideas, and then later, we will see that they are, in fact, the same.

Here are the two ideas. The first idea is that if you take a cone and you cut it with a plane, you get some sort of a shape. Right? You get some sort of a shape, and I said, "Well, it is an ellipse," and it is. All you know for sure, though, is that it's what you get when you take a cone and you cut it. This is the shape that you get.

Then we were talking about a totally different description of a curve. This description of a curve is the set of all the points so that the sum of the distances to two points is a constant. You see, that's a totally different kind of description of a curve, and right now, there's no reason for you to believe that when you cut a cone like this with a plane, that the exact shape of that curve should have anything to do with the shape of this curve. I mean, it's generally oval, but why would have that exact property, that every point on it has a constant distance to two fixed points? You see? There are two different descriptions. The cutting of a cone with a plane, and the set of all points so that the sum of the distances to two points is a constant.

Those are two different things. Why are they the same? That's the question.

We're going to prove this, and if you had geometry class in high school, and they proved this—and they may or may not have proved it, because it's complicated—what they probably did was to use equations, and you would use complicated equations, and it's hard. What I'm going to do is to show you that these two ideas are the same, in an extremely elegant way that will use no equations at all.

I'm hoping that you have the idea that what we're trying to do is to show that this intersection of a plane with a cone has the special property that every point on it has the sum of two distances.

First of all, if you take a cone, and you cut it with a plane, you get a curve. Even though I've drawn these two points on it for later use, there're no two points that come to mind as the two special points that are the sum of the distances, though. When you see a plane and a cone, what two points would you choose?

Here is this wonderful, wonderful proof, then. What you do is you take your right circular cone—I can't have this ball pass through the plane, but I have to imagine that this plane is already in the cone—and you pick a round sphere, a ball, and you make it exactly correct size so that when you nestle the ball in the cone, it just grazes this plane that's cutting through. It just touches it. You see? You see that we made this—actually, my wife made this; I think it's amazing. She made it so that it is exactly the right size, so that it just touches this plane in one point.

Then, what you do is you take a big ball, and you put it in the cone. It's too big, and you make it smaller, smaller, smaller, smaller, until it's just exactly the right size, so that it touches the plane from the top at exactly one point. It nestles into the cone, and just touches it exactly at one point. Now, this is something that is sort of like a miracle, that those two points are the *foci* of the ellipse, meaning that the foci are the two points so that the sum of the distances to those two points are constant. Those two are the ones.

Now, this is just sort of like a miracle. Why in the world is that true? It is, though, and so that is what we're going to see.

What we need to do now is to take a little excursion that's a slight side trip to look at a fact about the world, so let's just take the world, here. This is an example of the world. Suppose that we were in a spacecraft, for example, the space shuttle, floating above the world; we are looking down at the globe, and from our eyes, we just looked to each side of the horizon, of the globe, of the Earth. Suppose, for example, we wanted to go to the nearest point on the horizon.

Well, if this is a perfect sphere, let's just see if we can figure out where the nearest point on the horizon might be. When I'm going to do is pretend that this is at my eye, and then I'm just going to put this stick down to indicate the distance between my eye, here, and the horizon. Now, the horizon is exactly where it just touches, where it is just tangent as it goes by.

Now, if I look at this carefully, I can actually notice that this point and this point, these two points, seem about the same distance away, and in fact, intuitively, you might think, "Well, yes, in fact, they are exactly the same distance away," and they are. No matter what two points on the horizon I choose, and no matter what distance I am away from the Earth, the two points that just graze are exactly the same distance away.

In order to see that, though, this is the kind of example where you make an observation, and you have an intuitive idea that something is true, and one of the strategies of mathematics is to try to pin it down by looking at a simpler case, and then actually confirming that it is true. Instead of thinking about looking at the globe, then, let's go down to a simpler case that is a plainer version of this, namely, a circle. Suppose we take a circle, then, and we start looking at a circle.

Here we have a perfect circle, and what we're going to do is put this circle down, and do the same thing. We put our eyes right here, and we're going to say, "What is the distance between the two places that just graze the circle, the two sides?"

Well, look, if we do this here, I better get some things to mark it. Suppose we just take two places. I have just chosen an arbitrary distance away, and then I'm going to say that it hits here right about here, and I've got to make sure that I don't move it, and then here, it just hits right here, and let's just see if those are the same distance apart. Yes, they are exactly the same distance apart. This is a confirmation that that is true. In fact, there's a little graphic that can prove that this is true, and so on your screen, you will see that we can just do a little construction with triangles that can actually prove that the distance from any point external to the circle, to grazing the circle, is exactly the same.

Once we have proved this simple case, we can then show that it's true for the sphere case, which is the one that we were originally interested in, because, look here. When we did this process of taking the distance between our eye and just grazing the side of a sphere, what would happen if we just cut the sphere with a plane that contained these two bars? You see? Whenever you take a sphere, which is perfectly round in all directions, if you cut with a plane, of course, you get a circle. And we know the truth of the fact that if you just graze a circle, it's the same distance, then you also know that it is true for a sphere. Doing the easy case, then, of the plane [sic circle] has shown us why the same fact is true for the sphere.

Now let's begin by getting back to why this miraculous fact, that these two points are the foci of this ellipsis, is true. Once again, this is a complicated situation, so let's look at a simpler version of it. Well, what would a simpler version be? Here's a simpler version. It looks the same; a simpler version of a cone in the plane is just a "V," and a simpler version of a plane that cuts through is just a line segment. Thus, we can do the same property here. Instead of filling this with a bigger ball on top and a smaller ball on the bottom, we can find a bigger ball here. We make it just big enough to be tangent at the two points, and just tangent to that line. Do you see that? It's tangent to those two points, because it just fits in the triangle, and then it touches at this point.

Then, we make a circle that is just big enough to fit. Well, this one is too small. You see? It's too small, so we need to make it slightly bigger. Look, this one is just right, so that it just fits between the two lines, and it touches at this cutting line, at exactly one point, so you see that it's analogous. We're trying to prove something about a three-dimensional situation, and instead, we focus on a simpler case. This is a wonderful strategy of mathematics, and a strategy for dealing with all sorts of questions. First, concentrate on the simpler cases, so that you really understand them, and then that gives you the strength to apply it to a more complicated setting.

Now, here we go. Here's what we're going to see. The distance from this point right here, where this touches, to this point right here, is the same as the distance from this tangent point to this tangent point, from this one to this one. Those are the same, because these circles are nestled down in there, and so they are the same distance. Look, though. If you start at this point, the distance to this tangent point of the circle right here, that distance is the same as this distance. Right? Because this is what we just showed, that if you graze a circle at two different directions, you have the same distance.

Now, look at this big circle, though. It's the same thing. From this point, this just grazes up here to this distance, and is the same as the distance from the point along this blue line to where it just grazes this one. The sum of the distance from this point to where it grazes this circle, plus the distance from this point to where it grazes this circle, is equal to this distance plus this distance. Likewise, for this circle up here, it's the same thing. This distance is the same as this distance, and this distance is the same as the distance to the point of tangency here for the small circle, so the sum of those two, the sum of the distances to this tangency plus this tangency from this point is that much, and the sum of the distances from this point to this tangency plus this tangency is the same amount, so that they are equal.

Let's now see if we can apply our knowledge to the situation we really want. If we take an arbitrary point on this ellipse, and we go straight to the point of tangency of the ball, and then, we go straight up along the cone, all the way straight up, that straight line segment is equal in length to the distance to that point of tangency. If we go to the point of tangency of the small ball, then that length will be equal to the distance straight along the cone to this point of tangency, so that the sum of the distances from this point, and an arbitrary point on this supposed ellipse, to this point of tangency equals that, plus the distance from this point to the other point of tangency is this, so the sum is the distance from this circle, where this ball is nestled, to this circle.

No matter what point you choose along this ellipse, the sum is always going to be the distance from the top circle to the bottom circle. These round, blue circles, though, are the same distance apart all the way around, so for every point on the ellipse, the sum of the distances to those two points of tangency is constant, namely, the constant distance between those two blue circles.

Well, this is an amazing demonstration of the fact that this ellipse, in fact, is an ellipse, that it has the property that the sum of the distances to the two points of tangency are actually a constant, and it gives an example of finding the essential features of a complicated situation that really illustrate the fundamental reasons for something being true. It's a wonderful paradigm for what to seek when you're trying to understand the world.

Lecture Nine
Not-so-Platonic Relationships in Platonic Solids

Michael Starbird, Ph.D.

Scope:

Symmetry and regularity lie at the heart of classical beauty. We have an instinctive affinity for symmetrical objects—things that can be turned or reflected and return to their original shapes. The sphere is the ultimate in symmetry. From any vantage point, the sphere looks the same. If we forego the graceful constant curvature of the sphere and consider objects with flat sides, then how symmetric and graceful can they be? Here, we explore the *Platonic*, or *regular*, solids. These flat-sided, symmetrical solids have intrigued people for thousands of years.

The closer we look at the Platonic solids, the more we see in them. We will study them, first, by moving from the qualitative to the quantitative—how many edges, faces, vertices does each solid have? Then, we record our observations and discover surprising coincidences. In life, coincidences are flashing lights signaling us to look for reasons and relationships that reveal a deeper structure. In the Platonic solids, we find a surprising dual nature that turns these separate objects into a coherent collection.

Outline

I. Symmetry, the property that an object looks the same from different points of view, is an instinctively appealing feature of objects.

   A. Psychologists have done studies indicating that people find symmetrical faces beautiful.

   B. Symmetry is a fundamental principle in most perspectives on architecture, art, and culture.

   C. Mathematicians explore the idea of symmetry in the context of the shapes that form the basis of geometry. This lecture examines, in particular, the most symmetrical of three-dimensional shapes, the *Platonic solids*.

      1. Our exploration of these objectives moves us from the qualitative to the quantitative; we take a step forward, in our thinking, to more precision.

2. This exploration also points up the significance of coincidences, signals that we should look more deeply to explain the similarities we find.

II. We begin by looking at a simple case first, planar objects.

    A. The circle is the most symmetrical of planar figures.

    B. Among polygonal figures in the plane, the equilateral triangles, squares, pentagons, and all regular polygons have maximum symmetry.

    C. We could almost view the circle as an "infinity-gon," a figure with infinitely many sides of equal length.

III. After we have an idea of symmetry in the plane, we can generalize the idea to three dimensions.

    A. The sphere is the most symmetrical three-dimensional object.

    B. Analogous to polygons in the plane, what kind of solids can be made if each face is a polygon?

        1. A cube is probably the most familiar symmetrical solid. Like a die, it has 6 sides, or *faces*, and each face is a square.

        2. Further, every vertex of the cube has 3 faces, or *is incident to* 3 faces.

    C. The simplest of the regular solids, however, is the *tetrahedron*.

        1. The tetrahedron has 4 triangular faces.

        2. Every face is an equilateral triangle.

        3. This solid can be conceptualized as a pyramid over a triangle. A true pyramid has a square base and is not a regular solid.

        4. Every vertex of a tetrahedron is incident to 3 faces.

    D. The next regular solid is an *octahedron*, which has 8 faces, each of which is an equilateral triangle. Each vertex of an octahedron is incident to 4 faces. This solid looks similar to one pyramid sitting on top of another.

    E. The *dodecahedron* has 12 faces, each of which is a pentagon. Each vertex is incident to 3 pentagons.

    F. The *icosahedron* has 20 triangular faces. Each vertex is incident to 5 triangles.

G. Unlike planar figures, which could have infinitely many sides of equal length, the three-dimensional solids are limited to just these five. Lecture 10 will examine the reason that we have only five solids.

IV. When we have identified a collection of interesting objects, we can set about analyzing them to appreciate them with more nuance.

 A. One way to appreciate these objects more is to move from the qualitative to the quantitative. In this case, we want to count the features of the solids, their vertices, edges, and faces.

 B. Here is a chart that summarizes our results:

Solid	Vertices	Edges	Faces
Tetrahedron	4	6	4
Cube	8	12	6
Octahedron	6	12	8
Dodecahedron	20	30	12
Icosahedron	12	30	20

 C. We might use a more systematic approach, other than just counting, to determine the number of vertices and edges of some of these solids.

 1. For example, the dodecahedron has 12 faces, each with 5 edges. Because each edge is shared by exactly 2 faces, there are $\dfrac{(12 \times 5)}{2} = 30$ edges.

 2. Similarly, each face of the dodecahedron has 5 vertices. Each vertex is shared by exactly 3 faces; thus, there are $\dfrac{(12 \times 5)}{3} = 20$ vertices.

 3. For the icosahedron, we count 20 faces, each with 3 edges; thus, $\dfrac{(20 \times 3)}{2} = 30$ edges. We also count 5 faces for each vertex; thus, $\dfrac{(20 \times 3)}{5} = 12$.

V. Next, we move on to one of the most powerful strategies in mathematics, looking for patterns. These serve as red flags, signaling us that we should seek an underlying reason for similarities that we find.

A. In the chart on the Platonic solids, let's notice some patterns, beginning with the cube.

    1. Cubes have 6 faces and 8 vertices, while octahedrons have 6 vertices and 8 faces. Also, the cube and octahedron have the same numbers of edges, 12.

    2. Can we find a reason that the number of faces on the cube is equal to the number of vertices on the octahedron and vice versa?

    3. Imagine that you are in a room that is a cube. Look straight up and mark a point at the center of the ceiling. This point is a vertex of the octahedron.

    4. Now, mark similar points at the center of each of the four walls and the floor.

    5. You have now marked six dots, the same as the number of vertices of the octahedron. If we connect all the dots, we would, indeed, construct an octahedron.

    6. In your mind's eye, when you see a cube, you should also be able to visualize an octahedron contained within the cube. The figures are two visions of the same idea.

    7. The octahedron and cube, thus, share the property of *duality*.

B. We ask ourselves: Is it possible that the dodecahedron is related in a similar way to the icosahedron?

    1. If we return to our chart, we see that the dodecahedron has 12 faces, 30 edges, and 20 vertices and the icosahedron has 12 vertices, 30 edges, and 20 faces.

    2. We now know how to visualize these figures, and we can see that the icosahedron fits inside the dodecahedron.

C. We can also think about why dual objects must be part of the Platonic solids. If you mark a vertex in the middle of a face of any solid and you connect it to the centers of the adjacent faces, you will produce another solid.

D. We know that for the dodecahedron, every vertex is incident to 3 faces; thus, the dual figure will be made of triangles.

E. What about the tetrahedron? It is self-dual.

F. This lecture has shown us some beautifully symmetric regular solids and taught us to look for patterns as a way of exploring the world.

Suggested Reading:

Edward B. Burger and Michael Starbird, *The Heart of Mathematics: An invitation to effective thinking*, Key College Publishing, Section 4.5, "The Platonic Solids Turn Amorous: Discovering the symmetry and interconnections among the Platonic Solids."

Questions to Consider:

1. For each of the Platonic solids, draw a picture of how you can unfold it in various ways so it lies flat on the plane and illustrate how it could be folded up to create the solid.

2. Suppose you allow different numbers of triangles to come together at different vertices of a solid; then show how to produce solids with arbitrarily large numbers of triangular faces.

Lecture Nine—Transcript
Not-so-Platonic Relationships in Platonic Solids

Symmetry is a property that seems to lie at the heart of beauty, and particularly, a classical version of beauty, but there is some sense in which symmetry may actually be something that is instinctively a feature to which we human beings respond. There was a professor of psychology who did the following experiment. She took a collection of faces, and then averaged the faces, meaning that she took all these photographs of faces—and everybody's face is actually a little irregular—and she took a sort of computer average of the faces to make an average face. Then, she asked people to evaluate it for its beauty, and she discovered that that face was viewed as extremely beautiful. Part of the reason was that it was completely symmetrical, because when you do an average over a lot of people, the symmetry lines that differ from individual to individual get averaged out, and so you have this completely average, symmetric image.

It could well be that human beings instinctively look for the kind of regularity and symmetry, and respond to this in a favorable way. Certainly, from classical times to the present time, this concept of symmetry as the underlying sense that creates beauty has been present in architecture, and art, and in all forms of the discussion of beauty.

First of all, then, let's talk about what symmetry is. Symmetry means that if you have an object, it looks the same when you look at it from different points of view, or maybe, sometimes symmetry means that you can switch sides, and it still looks the same. Symmetry is that kind of regularity.

In this lecture, we are going to be talking about some of the most beautiful objects that have intrigued human beings for thousands of years, and those are the *Platonic solids*, the *regular solids*. These are objects that are as symmetrical as solid things can get, and we will discuss them in detail. The investigation of these beautiful objects, though, also brings an idea of how it is that we can investigate issues more deeply.

The first one we have encountered before, and that is to count things, to move from the qualitative sense to the quantitative sense. When we do that, that moment, from qualitative to quantitative, really takes us a step further in precision, and nuance, and interest. That, then, is the first thing.

The second thing is when we find coincidences. We find things that seem to be the same, but we don't know exactly why. Then, those are shining lights that say, "Come on. Let's look and see what the underlying reason is that these two things are equivalent."

Those two ideas, then, of moving from qualitative to quantitative, and taking coincidences and then investigating them because we seek an underlying understanding of why they are true, and following patterns, are all strategies of thinking that can lead us a great deal of distance.

Let's now turn our attention again to symmetry, and as always, we will start with a simple case, which in this case will be planar objects, flat objects. What is the most symmetrical object that we can think of that is flat? Well, it's simple. The most symmetrical object that you can think of is the circle. A perfect circle is perfectly symmetrical. Wherever you gaze at it, from whatever direction you look, it's exactly the same, so that it has as much symmetry as it is possible to have.

If we forego a circle, something that's actually round, and we insist that what we are considering are made of flat pieces, straight pieces, then we turn instead to the idea of the regular polygons, for example, an equilateral triangle. This is a triangle; it has exactly three sides that are all equal to each other, and it has as much symmetry as a three-sided object can have.

Well, we move on to the square. These are all familiar shapes. The square has four sides, all the same length, and it is as symmetric as a four-sided figure can be. It's quite attractive, I think, don't you? Then, we have a pentagon, five-sided figure. You see? One, two, three, four, five. Five sides, equal length, and so that is an attractive object. It has as much symmetry as a five-sided figure can have.

Here's a hexagon, made of six sides. Notice, in fact, that there's no reason to end. We can have a seven-sided figure, an eight-sided figure, a nine-sided figure, a ten-sided figure. Is there a 100-sided figure? A million-sided figure? In fact, one way to think about a circle is that, in a way, a circle is an "infinity-gon." It's what you would get if you actually went to infinity, and had infinitely many sides that were all equidistant.

In the plane, then, we have as many regular planar objects as we wish, one for every counting number. Having investigated the two-dimensional arena, now let's move to three-dimensional space, and think about the most symmetrical object we can think of in three dimensions, which is the sphere. Well, the sphere is a beautifully symmetrical object. No matter what way we look at it, it looks the same as from any other vantage point. It is beautifully symmetric, but it's actually hard to make a sphere if you are making it out of cardboard or plywood, because it doesn't have any flat sides.

Let's, then, go through the same process that we went through before, and talk about what would be the most symmetrical object we could construct, where every face of the object is flat, and a polygon, and just has a finite number of edges. How could we make objects like that?

We'll put the sphere aside, and start thinking about symmetrical objects. This is the most familiar of these objects. This is a cube. We all see cubes all the time, and the room in which we sit is probably somewhat like a cube. A cube is somewhat like a die. It has six sides, and each side is a square. In addition, at every vertex of the cube, you can see that there are the same number of *faces* coming out. There are three sides coming out from every vertex, and if you turn the cube and you look at it, look at every single vertex, it looks exactly the same as any other vertex. Thus, it has perfect symmetry for an object that has square sides. This is the cube.

The cube is actually not the simplest of the regular solids, though. The simplest of the regular solids is a little bit less familiar, perhaps. It is the tetrahedron. A *tetrahedron*, here, has four triangular sides, and every side is an equilateral triangle, and four of them make this tetrahedron. Now, you might think of the tetrahedron, if you put it down like this, like a pyramid over a triangle. That is a way to conceptualize it. You see, a pyramid, like the pyramids of Giza, has a square base. That's a pyramid, so that's not a regular solid. A pyramid is not a regular solid because there are triangular sides that come up, but the base is square. It's not the case that every face is identical to every other face, whereas this figure has every face identical to every other face, and every vertex—the points are called vertices—has exactly three faces coming out from it.

These are the first two regular solids, then. The next regular solid is this one. It's called *octahedron*. And you can see the Greek roots of these words: "octa-," from eight. It has eight faces, and each face of an octahedron is, again, a triangle, an equilateral triangle. This reminds us of these pyramids again, because if you wish to construct an octahedron, the way we would do it is that you would take two pyramids. You have a pyramid on the top and a pyramid on the bottom, and you see that they fit together right here in the middle. There's the square in the middle, a pyramid underneath, and a pyramid on top of, and this forms this eight-sided, symmetrical figure, the octahedron. Isn't that beautiful? I think these are great just to look at.

Then as we move up, the next one that we have has 12 sides. Now, this is getting more complicated. It's sort of interesting. Here, each face is a pentagon, a five-sided figure. See? Each face is a pentagon. Each vertex *is incident to* three different pentagons. If I look at this from any vantage point of any vertex, it looks identical to any other vantage point. There are 12 sides to this, 12 pentagonal sides that make this beautiful *dodecahedron*: "do-," two, "dec-," ten, and you add them. In this case, "do-" and "dec-" will make 12. I'll remind you that there are 12 sides to the dodecahedron.

Then, we come to this object, and this is an *icosahedron*. It has 20 faces that are triangles, 20 triangular faces. Every vertex has five triangles that come out from it, so that if I look at it from the vantage point of any vertex, I see five triangles coming out, and has this beautiful symmetry. Beautiful symmetry.

Now, I wonder if I should just go on and, maybe we should just talk about these. Maybe there are a lot more of them. Maybe the next one has 30 sides, or 50 sides. Do you think we should go on? Maybe I should just talk about these here. Well, actually I think I should just stick to these, and the reason is that these are all there are, unlike the case for the plane, where you could have a triangle, you could have a square, you could have a five-sided figure, six-sided figure, seven-, eight-, nine-; you could have any number. You could have infinitely many different figures, each of which is completely symmetrical, but for the three-dimensional figures, this is all she wrote. This is all there are. There are no more than these five.

In fact, there were known to be only five of these regular solids back in ancient times. Plato was so interested in these, and thought that it made some special significance to the number of five, that he associated the elements of the Greek world, one with each of the regular solids. It has an historical allure, then, that has endured for thousands of years.

These, then, are the five regular solids. The explanation for the reason that there are five regular solids will have to wait until the next lecture. I will actually give a very interesting proof of the reason that there are only five, but for now, we want to explore them, and when I say, "explore them," this is an example of an instance where we have been introduced to an idea in the world. We see something here. These are the regular solids.

How do we go about exploring them? How can we take our experience of the world and understand it more deeply? Well, we've talked about this before, and one of the best ways to do it is to become quantitative rather than just qualitative. I think it's great to just feel these, and look at them, and hold them. That's a terrific way to start to understand these objects.

We can take a much bigger step forward, though, if we start to count, to measure things. Well, what would we count in these objects? We know that there are five of them. That's one count, but in understanding one of these objects, what kinds of things would we count? Well, it's natural. We would count the features that we notice.

The features that we notice from this object, this tetrahedron, are: the vertices, the edges, and the faces. So let's go ahead and count them. Let's count them for this one. This is a tetrahedron. Let's see. It has one, two, three, four vertices; it has one, two, three, four, five, six edges; and it has four faces: one, two, three, four. Now we have sort of a quantitative appreciation for this, as well as see it just as a whole.

Let's move on to the cube, and do the same thing. We will count. Let's count how many vertices there are. There are one, two, three, four, five, six, seven, eight vertices. How many edges are there? One, two, three, four, five, six, seven, eight, nine, ten, eleven, twelve. There are 12 edges. We already know, because of the dice, that there are six faces to them, and let's just verify that. There's one at the bottom, that's one. There are four around the sides. That's five altogether, four plus one, five, and one at the top is six, so there are six faces to the cube, as we knew.

We'll move on to the octahedron. The octahedron has how many vertices? One, two, three, four around the belt, where these two pyramids are on top of each other. There are four vertices there, then there's a vertex on top, and a vertex below, for a total of six vertices. There are eight faces, the four faces that are facing upward, the four that come down the inverted pyramid, so that is a total of eight faces. How many edges are there? Well, let's see. There are four edges coming out from this vertex, so that's four. Then there are four around here; four more is eight. Then there are four that are facing downward, for a total of 12.

Well, let's see. We'll just do a little bit more of this. This is the dodecahedron. If we hold it like this, we can see that the dodecahedron has 12 faces. One, and then there are five faces; each one is a pentagon, five sides, and so there are five pentagons coming out from this one face. I'm holding it upright. There are five pentagons here, so that's a total of six. Then, underneath, we have another six. We have a pentagon on the base, and we have five surrounding it, for a total of another six, so that altogether, we have 12 faces.

It's about time to be a little more systematic in our counting, because we could easily lose track of, for example, how many edges there are. We've got so many, maybe we could mark them, but it would be a little bit complicated to stand here and count the number of edges. Can we think of a systematic method for counting the edges? Well, sure. Here's a very simpleminded method, a very simpleminded method, namely, every face has five edges. There are 12 faces, 12 times 5 is 60.

Well, okay, that's almost right, but it's not quite right. Why is that not really the number of edges? Why was it an incorrect argument to say that was the number of edges? Well, because look at this edge right here, for example. We counted this edge once as one of the five edges for this face, but we also counted it again as one of the edges for this face, so we counted it twice, but we counted it exactly twice, so this was a great example of making a fruitful mistake. We just multiplied the number of faces, 12 times the number of edges for each one, five, to get 60, but then we noticed, "Oh, we made a mistake. That's not really correct, because this edge was counted twice." Therefore, we compensate, namely, divide by 2, because we counted it exactly twice. We counted every single edge exactly twice. Thus, the number of edges is 5 times 12, but divided by 2, which is a total of 30, and indeed, there are 30 edges to this object, a dodecahedron.

Well, once we have the concept of systematically analyzing how many different things there are, let's do this same thing, and see if we can figure out how to compute how many vertices there are. Well, we have a method in mind. The method was to make a mistake, and then compensate for our mistake. How would we count the number vertices? Well, look, it's the same thing. Every face has five vertices. There are 12 faces; 5 times 12 is 60, again. Once again, we have made a mistake. What was our mistake? Our mistake was that every vertex was counted three times, because it was counted as being part of this face, was counted as being part of this face, and counted as being part of this face, so that this vertex was counted three times, this one was counted three times, and every one was counted three times, so that 5 times 12 divided by 3 will give us the correct number of vertices; 5 times 12 is 60, divided by 3 is 20. There are, indeed, 20 of these vertices, these white balls, in this dodecahedron, so this is a dodecahedron.

Now, when we get to this even more complicated icosahedron, we're in a position to count them rather quickly, because we've developed strength. We've developed what we mean by counting. We can count the number of faces. There are 20 faces. Each face has three sides to it, so 20 times 3 is 60, again, but each edge is counted twice, so divided by 2 is 30. How many vertices are there? Well, on an icosahedron, every vertex has five faces coming into it, so we could say, since we know that every face is a triangle, that there are 20 of them, so once again, 3 times 20—three vertices for every triangle— is 60, but now, we have to divide by 5, because every vertex is counted 5 times; 5 into 60 goes 12 times, so there are 12 vertices to an icosahedron.

Well, this was a good exercise, because what we have now is a little table that summarizes our findings, and now we're going to do something that is one of the most powerful methods of finding things out in the world: you look at something you know, and you see whether you can find some unexpected patterns, some serendipitous equalities, and if you do find them, then they are the shining lights that tell you to seek a reason.

Well, let's look at our chart here:

Solid	Vertices	Edges	Faces
Tetrahedron	4	6	4
Cube	8	12	6
Octahedron	6	12	8
Dodecahedron	20	30	12
Icosahedron	12	30	20

If you look at the number of vertices, edges, and faces in, for example, the cube and the octahedron, you notice something about them. Let's read them off. For the cube, there are eight vertices, 12 edges, and six faces. For the octahedron, there are six vertices, 12 edges again, and eight faces.

Now, first of all, the three numbers appear in both sets. The only difference is that the number of vertices of the cube is equal to the number of faces of the octahedron. The number of vertices of the octahedron is equal to the number of faces of the cube.

Now, let's think. Is there a reason for that, or is it just luck? Can we think about whether there's a reason? We have seen this amazing equality between the number of vertices of the octahedron, and the number of faces of the cube. Let's see if we can actually render that equality, physically make the equality.

Let's think about a room. Suppose you're in a cubicle room. Most rooms are somewhat cubicle. Let's see if we can actually physically create that correspondence between the number of vertices of the octahedron and the faces of the cube.

Look at the ceiling. Look straight up at the center point of the ceiling, and put a dot there. That's going to be a vertex of our octahedron. Now, look at this wall over here, and put a dot right in the middle of that wall, and put a dot in the middle of this wall, and put a dot in the middle of this wall, and put a dot in the middle of this wall. Now, put a dot on the floor. Do you see how many dots you put? Six.

Now, the idea is that six was the number of vertices of the octahedron. Can we construct an octahedron using those dots? Well, yes, we can. We take the center of the ceiling, and connect it by a straight line to the center of that wall, and then connect it by a straight line to the center of that wall, by a straight line to the center of that wall, and by a straight line to the center of that wall. Then, if we connect the centers of these walls to each other—this one to this one, to this one, to this one, to this one, we have surrounded ourselves by a pyramid. If we sat in there, we would see a pyramid coming down from the center of the ceiling turned diagonally in the room, sitting on top of us, and then similarly, coming down to the center of the floor, there would be an inverted pyramid, that we see in our mind's eye.

When we see this cube in our mind's eye, then, we see the existence of this octahedron that is in there, that is entailed by the existence of the cube, is the essence of the octahedron. They are two visions of the same idea.

Now, let's actually do it. We have physically made one right here, so you can see this relationship between the cube and the octahedron. You can see how that octahedron just floats in the middle of the cube, where every vertex of the octahedron is centered in the center of the cube in which it sits.

These objects have this amazing dual property, that the octahedron is the dual of the cube. Well, now, look. When we see a relationship like that, we just can't help but explore it some more, and we ask ourselves, "Is it possible that the dodecahedron, that very complicated object that has pentagonal faces, is related to the icosahedron?"

Well, look at the numbers. We will go back to our chart, and sure enough, we see an amazing coincidence, but in our hearts, we're saying, "You know, that's not a coincidence. There's a reason." We see, though, in our chart—look. The dodecahedron has 12 faces, 20 vertices, and 30 edges, whereas the icosahedron has the opposite. By the opposite, I mean that the number of vertices in an icosahedron is 12. That's the same as the number of faces in the dodecahedron, and vice versa. The number of faces in the icosahedron is 20, and that's equal to the number of vertices in the dodecahedron, which is 20, and they both have the same number of edges. They both have 30 edges.

You see? Those are coincidences that we can't ignore, but we now know how to actually make geometrical and real that relationship. What do we do? We take one of these objects, we put a vertex in the center of each face, and we connect it up. We know for sure when we do that that we're going to get another figure that has symmetry. Here, we've actually made it. I should say, my wife and daughter actually made it, and here it is. The blue outer one here, that I'm pointing to right here, is a dodecahedron. It has 12 pentagonal faces, and inside it, you see, floating, an icosahedron, where I have a vertex; one of these vertex balls is in the center of each face of the dodecahedron.

Now, if we think about it, this physically creates it. We know that it is true here, just by physically looking at this object. We see that this is true, but we can also think about why it must be true, why dual objects must be part of the reality of a Platonic solid, because if you have any solid, and you put a vertex in the middle of the face, and then you connect it to the center of the adjacent faces, you would produce another solid.

If you have a solid, though, like this dodecahedron, that has all of this symmetry, every vertex has exactly three faces coming out, then, the dual figure is going to be made of triangles, because the centers of those three faces, of the dodecahedron, are going to be joined up like this. See? A center of this face, a center of this face, a center of this one. The ones that surround this vertex of the dodecahedron are the vertices of one face of the dual figure. So, there's a one-to-one correspondence between the vertices of this figure and the faces of the dual figure.

Additionally, notice that these edges just cross. They are perpendicular to each other. Every edge is crossed by another edge. There's exactly one. That's why the edges are in one-to-one correspondence. That's why there are the same number of edges in the dodecahedron as in the icosahedron. We saw that one-to-one correspondence, that reason that there are the same number of edges, in the octahedron as the cube, because, you see, these edges correspond. That edge, and the edge that crosses diagonally, correspond. This is an amazing way, then, of seeing that when you see a regular figure like this, that its dual is part of its nature.

Wait a minute, though. We missed one. You can't let yourself not look at the last figure. The last figure is the tetrahedron, but it's all by itself. What's happening here? We know we could do the construction of taking its dual, putting a vertex in the middle of each face. What happens? You should see in your mind's eye that you know what happens. You know what has to happen. It's got to have a dual figure. That dual figure has to be completely symmetrical, and be a regular solid, and there's nothing left. It's the last one. It's self-dual. The dual of the tetrahedron is another tetrahedron.

This lecture, then, has shown some of these beautifully symmetric regular solids, but also has taught us a way of exploring things, by counting, by looking at patterns that we just see among the numbers that we have created, and then by trying to explain them. We see that when we take an object, a related concept—in this case the dual of the object—is inherent in the very existence of that first object. These are wonderful strategies for investigating the world.

Lecture Ten
Hunting for a Sixth Platonic Solid

Michael Starbird, Ph.D.

Scope:

For centuries, the Platonic solids inspired thinkers with a mystical allure. Plato apparently attempted to relate them to the fundamental components that he believed made up the world. The Pythagoreans, who knew that there were exactly five regular solids and no others, held them in awe. Two millennia later, Johannes Kepler shared this sense of awe for the Platonic solids.

Although Kepler is remembered best for his laws of planetary motion, he was proudest of his book *Mysterium Cosmographicum*. In it, he proposed a theory involving the regular solids to explain the structure of the solar system, which at the time, was believed to consist of six planets. His work appealed to a mystical power of the five regular solids that he felt were related to the intervals between the planets' orbits. Sadly, Kepler's theory was refuted in 1781 when another planet, Uranus, was discovered. Unfortunately for Kepler's theory, there will always be only five regular solids.

Outline

I. In this lecture, we will learn why there are only five regular solids. Along the way, we will discover three strategies to enhance our thinking.

   A. The first of these strategies is to analyze the reasons for our mistakes.

   B. The second is to seek the essential. In this method, we shift perspectives from a rigid domain to a much looser domain, then apply our findings back to the original question.

   C. The third strategy involves understanding a finished product by following the building process that created the product and looking for properties that are preserved during the course of construction.

II. Why are there only five regular solids?

   A. Recall that each face of a regular solid is a regular polygon and that every vertex has the same number of edges and faces incident to it.

B. Let's begin with a method of proof that involves the building blocks of the regular solids—triangles, squares, and so on—and see why we can put only certain numbers of these together to create regular solids.

  1. Suppose we specify that each face of the solid we are going to construct must be a triangle. Could we construct a regular solid in which six equilateral triangles meet at each vertex?

  2. In the tetrahedron, three triangles meet at each vertex. In the octahedron, four triangles meet at a vertex, and in the icosahedron, five triangles meet at a vertex.

  3. If we attempt to make a solid in which six equilateral triangles come together at a vertex, we see the impossibility, because those triangles will lie flat. Given that each angle in an equilateral triangle is 60 degrees, the total of six triangles will be 360 degrees.

C. Suppose we specify that each face must be a square.

  1. If three squares come together at each vertex, we construct a cube.

  2. If four squares meet at a vertex, they lie flat and cannot create a solid. No other regular solids with square faces are possible.

D. If we use the pentagon for the face of our solid, as in a dodecahedron, three is the most that could meet at one vertex. The measure of the angles of more than three pentagons is more than 360 degrees.

E. Any regular polygon with six or more sides cannot be used to make any solid because even three of these meeting at a vertex would comprise more than 360 degrees, which means that they cannot be part of a solid.

F. This analysis provides a physical argument for why there are only five Platonic solids.

III. An alternative argument is interesting in that, surprisingly, it does not appear to use most of the properties of a solid object.

  A. We draw a random shape with eyes closed and without lifting the marker off the paper. We then mark a dot at each point where the line we drew crosses itself and at the beginning and ending points.

B. If we count the dots we have marked, subtract the edges between the dots, and add all the regions of the drawing, the result will be 2.

C. Our drawing has 8 dots, or vertices (V). It has 13 edges (E) and 7 regions (F), including the region outside the drawing. We can predict that if we compute $V - E + F$, the result will be 2, and it is: $8 - 13 + 7 = 2$.

D. If we view the drawing as a constructed object, we'll see that this relationship is always true.

   1. When we began the drawing, we had one vertex. The equation for just this beginning point of the drawing would be $1 - 0 + 1 = 2$.

   2. If we add the first edge and its final vertex, the resulting equation is $2 - 1 + 1 = 2$. The addition of one more edge and one more vertex results in a net change of 0.

   3. As long as we continue to add one edge and one vertex, we maintain the property that $V - E + F = 2$.

   4. If we connect two edges at one vertex, we create a new region, or face, in our drawing, which again, maintains the original property.

E. This insight, that $V - E + F = 2$, is called the *Euler characteristic*. The proof that we have just seen is known as a *proof by induction*.

IV. How does this proof apply to the regular solids?

   A. We return to the chart about the regular solids and make an observation:

Solid	V	E	F	$V-E+F$
Tetrahedron	4	6	4	2
Cube	8	12	6	2
Octahedron	6	12	8	2
Dodecahedron	20	30	12	2
Icosahedron	12	30	20	2

   B. The regular solids seem to have the same characteristic in the vertices, edges, and faces as our random drawing did, but these solids are not flat, as our drawing was.

      1. Can we generalize our earlier analysis to the three-dimensional solids?

      2. Imagine that we conduct our analysis on a sphere. Do we find any difference? The answer is no. The Euler characteristic remains true on a sphere.

C. How does this characteristic apply to a three-dimensional solid?

      1. If we imagine that we inflated a cube into a sphere, its edges and vertices would still have the same Euler characteristic as a sphere.

      2. Any solid, regular or not, will satisfy the condition $V - E + F = 2$.

D. We will now use that insight to prove that there are only five solids.

      1. Even drawing on the sphere, using rounded lines, we could draw no more than five regular solids with every vertex and every region having the same number of edges.

      2. Suppose that we have drawn on a sphere a figure that has edges and vertices that correspond to one of the regular solids.

      3. Every vertex in this drawing would have the same number of edges, because that is a property of being regular. Every region would also have the same number of edges forming the region.

      4. Let s equal the number of sides in each of the regions in our drawing; let c equal the number of edges that emanate from every vertex.

      5. Remember that we can find the number of edges by multiplying the number of vertices by the number of edges that emanate from each vertex and dividing by 2:
$$E = \frac{cV}{2}.$$

      6. We count the vertices by multiplying the number of faces by the number of sides and dividing by c:
$$F = \frac{cV}{s}.$$

7. If we now plug E and F in the Euler formula, we see that
$$V = V - \frac{cV}{2} + \frac{cV}{s} = 2.$$

8. Doing a bit of algebra, we can deduce that $2(s + c) > cs$.

9. If we plug in numbers, we see the following: If s (the number of sides) = 3, c can be 3, 4, or 5, and the inequality works. If $s = 4$, c can only be 3; and if $s = 5$, c can only be 3. Any other numbers for c will not satisfy the inequality in $2(s + c) > cs$.

E. The Euler characteristic is a restriction that tells us that only these five combinations of faces and numbers of vertices and edges will result in regular solids.

V. One scholar who was particularly intrigued by the Platonic solids was Johannes Kepler, the 16th-century astronomer.

   A. Kepler found a way to use the regular solids to explain the sizes of the orbits of the planets by nesting the five regular solids inside one another.

     1. Starting with a sphere, he put a regular solid around it, then circumscribed that with another sphere.

     2. He continued this process, thus producing six spheres.

     3. By choosing the proper order of the regular solids, he was able to show that the radii of the six spheres corresponded fairly accurately to the sizes of the orbits of the then-known planets.

   B. One other intriguing feature of the regular solids can be seen in the icosahedron.

     1. If we balance an icosahedron on an edge, we see, spanning across it, another parallel edge on the opposite side.

     2. If we join the ends of these edges, we find that we have created a Golden Rectangle!

     3. If we look carefully, we see that there are three such Golden Rectangles in the icosahedron.

     4. These rectangles fit together in the *Borromean rings*: They won't come apart, yet no two of them are linked to each other.

5. This fact is an amazing convergence of ideas about the regular solids with the Golden Rectangle.

C. Finally, we close with the important connection between the regular solids and a soccer ball.

    1. A soccer ball is really an icosahedron with the tip of each vertex cut off, forming 12 pentagons and 12 hexagons.

    2. The regular solids have intrigued thinkers for millennia.

Suggested Reading:

Edward B. Burger and Michael Starbird, *The Heart of Mathematics: An invitation to effective thinking*, Key College Publishing, Section 4.5, "The Platonic Solids Turn Amorous: Discovering the symmetry and interconnections among the Platonic Solids."

Questions to Consider:

1. Look at a soccer ball. Take the number of vertices, subtract the number of edges, add the number of faces. What do you get? This counting can be tricky, so think of a systematic method.

2. Is it possible to draw a connected graph in the plane with an odd number of faces, an even number of vertices, and an even number of edges? If so, draw one; if not, explain why not.

Lecture Ten—Transcript
Hunting for a Sixth Platonic Solid

In the last lecture, we were introduced to the beautiful Platonic solids, these five regular solids that all display the kind of symmetry that appeals so much to the human spirit. For each of these solids, remember that the defining property is that each face of each solid is the same as every other face, and each vertex has the same number of edges emitting from it. For example, in this tetrahedron, there are three edges that come out from every vertex.

Well, the five regular solids have held a hypnotic allure to people for millennia, and particularly, in ancient days, the fact that there were only five of them with such an appealing insight that they associated these five with the fundamental view of what makes up nature.

In particular, Plato thought that each of these five regular solids was associated with one of the elements of the time. Specifically, the tetrahedron was fire. That was fire. The octahedron, air. The icosahedron, water. This solid cubicle structure, earth. Finally, the fifth element, the quintessence, the dodecahedron. Plato, then, associated an element with each of these five regular solids.

Now, the question that still puzzles us in this sequence of lectures is: Why are there only five solids? We've said that there are only five, but we haven't actually yet proved that there are only five regular solids.

In the course of investigating that question, of actually seeing that indeed that is the case, that there are only five, that there can be only five, and there will always be only five, in proving that, we're going to see several methods of thinking that are intriguing, and are apt and appropriate for dealing with worlds well beyond mathematics.

One method is to try things and fail. Making a mistake, and then learning from the mistake, and seeing why that attempt fails, is an excellent way to force us to see what is true. That is a terrific strategy for thinking.

The second one is to seek essential ingredients. Seek the essence. Maybe like this one, the quintessential element. We are seeking the essential, and one thing that we will find in proving why there are only five regular solids is that in some sense, in one method of proof, we can see that the reason there are only five regular solids doesn't even correspond to the fact that these are made of flat, regular pieces. There's an essential feature that makes it impossible to make five of them that deals with much more amorphic things, with round things, with curvy lines, and why those two things are associated, the idea that you can use analyses about curved lines to deal with something as rigid as these regular solids is an interesting insight; and it shows that often, the essence of an issue that you are looking at may appear to not really be related to what you at first believed to be the essence of it.

The final lesson in regard to how to construct ideas is to follow a construction process. If you're building something complicated, sometimes you can get an insight into the first building block, and you can see something about it, and then, you can say, "When I add the next building block to it, some feature remains the same, has the same essential ingredient." Then, if you can prove that every time you take just one more step in your building process, if you can prove that during that one step, it retains some feature, that you know that the built object, that may include 1000 steps, will still retain the same feature that the original object had, the original piece had, and we will use that strategy of thinking in doing this analysis that leads to the proof that there are only five regular solids.

Let's begin, now, with trying to analyze why we couldn't have six regular solids. The first proof will be more direct, and is the one that you would more naturally think of. Namely, we're going to start with the building blocks for the regular solids—triangles, squares, pentagons, and so on—and just try to put them together, and then, after we try, we will see that we can't put too many of them together. We can't create more than we have.

Let's start with triangles. If you take six equilateral triangles, you might ask the question: Could there be a regular solid in which six edges come from each vertex? You see, in the tetrahedron, there are exactly three triangles that come from each vertex. In the octahedron, there are exactly four triangles that come from each vertex. And in the icosahedron, there are exactly five triangles that come from each vertex. So you might ask the question: Would it be possible to have six triangles that come out of each vertex?

Let's just take six triangles and assemble them, and just see what happens. If we assemble them—here I am assembling these six triangles; four, five, six—you see what happens is that it is now flat, because each angle is 60 degrees in an equilateral triangle, and if you put six of them around, you get 360 degrees. It's flat, so it never folds up, and can't possibly fold up to create a solid. That's a proof of why you can't have more than five triangles coming out from one vertex, and making a new solid. There's no hope in making a solid that has six triangles.

Let's try squares. You know the cube; the cube is the only regular solid that has square faces. There are three squares that come out of each corner of a cube. You see that every day; if you look in a corner of a room, you see three squares that come out of it. If you tried to make a regular solid where, at each vertex, there were four squares coming out, you would put them together, and you would see that, once again, you would have something that is flat. It would never fold up on itself, so you could not have more than three coming out from each vertex.

Finally, if you have pentagons, any pentagon has angles such that if you had more than three of them, of course, it would be too much. It would be more than 360 degrees, so that you couldn't have four pentagons all coming around one vertex. They wouldn't close up at all. In fact, you couldn't even make it flat.

Finally, you might say, "Well, is it possible to have a regular solid where each face has six sides, as a hexagon, or seven sides, or eight sides?" Well, let's see what would happen with six sides. If we had hexagons, and we made three of them put together, you know that every vertex has to have at least three things coming out from it. If there were only two, it would be squashed flat. If there were three, then, it would be flat again, and so, it wouldn't fold up. Therefore, you cannot have a regular solid that has hexagonal faces.

Thus, this is the first kind of argument that can be used to show that, indeed, there can be only five regular solids. By the way, I should say—I didn't actually mention this—that if you start out with, say, three squares, coming out from a vertex, then everything else is forced. If you decided, "Okay, I'm going to make a solid, and I'm going to have three squares coming out," well, you would have the three squares, and it's rigid. They have to be in a specific place. Then, you can go to a vertex there, and say, "Well, I need one more square," and you put it in, and you need one more square, and you construct the cube. There are no choices in the way that you construct it, and in fact, every one of the possible collections of triangles coming out from a vertex, or three squares coming out from a vertex, and three pentagons coming out from a vertex, each one of those does, in fact, create a regular solid that we see here.

Therefore, that is one kind of argument that leads to the fact that there are only five regular solids. What I'd like to do now, though, is to take a completely different turn. I'm going to look at a kind of a world that seems completely unconnected to these regular solids with the straight lines. This may seem like a diversion at first, then, but as they say in court, "We will tie it up later." We'll connect it up later.

Here's what I'm going to do. I'm going to take a marker and this piece of paper, and I'm going to draw a doodle, and I'm going to do with my eyes closed. I'm going to do it with my eyes closed, but I'm going to do it, and you will be very impressed that I will be able to say something about the final picture even though I've drawn it with my eyes completely closed. No cheating. Okay? Here I go. Ready? I am closing my eyes, so I'm drawing, which I'm doing with my eyes completely closed. Isn't this beautiful? This drawing—oh, look at that. That is just gorgeous. Now, I would like each of you to do this at home. Just close your eyes and make a doodle.

Then, I'm going to be able to predict something about it, and I'll tell you what it's going to be, that I'm going to count some features of this picture, and I'll bet that I can predict something that happened in your picture. Let's go ahead and do some counting. Here's what we're going to do. Were going to first to count how many times there is a crossing, so that every crossing, I put a dot. See this big dot here? I am making these big dots wherever there's a crossing. Dot … dot … dot … dot, and then I'm also making a dot at the end points, at each end point. Here's an end point, and here's an end point. I have made a dot at each end point.

Now, what I like to do, and would like you to do if you have drawn your own picture is to count various features of this picture. The first thing you want to count is how many dots there are, and for a mysterious reason, we will call the number of dots the name V. You may wonder, "Well, why in the world do we say V is the number of dots?" We'll see. The dots are going to be V, and let's count them. One, two, three, four, five, six, seven, eight. There are eight dots, and so, V is equal to 8. Whatever you've drawn, no matter how complicated, count the number of dots.

Next, count the number of edges (E) that you have. The edges are the things between dots, so we just go ahead and count them. We just go ahead and mark them; you see, this is an edge between dots. One, two, three, four, five, six, seven, eight, nine—and by the way, if you just travel along the path that you drew, you can't miss any—eleven, twelve, thirteen. There are 13 edges. You see? Thirteen edges. Then, if you count how many regions you have created in this drawing— well, the number of regions—there's one big region outside. Don't neglect to count the outside region. That's region number one. Then, you have some other regions here. Here's number two. Here's a region, number three. You see, this is a region. Number four, five, six, and seven. There are seven regions created in this drawing, and for some mysterious reason, we will call that F.

Now, what I'm going to predict happened, if you drew this in your own home, is that if we compute the number V minus E plus F, ($V-E+F$), we will get the number 2. No matter what your drawing was, you will get the number 2. We will confirm it here: 8 minus 13 is -5 plus 7 is indeed the number 2.

Of course, it's very mysterious that I was able to predict the number, but it might not be too exciting, because you don't know why I was able to do it, or even that it's true. Maybe I just knew how to draw this particular figure.

Let's show that no matter what you draw, no matter what doodle you drew, you will always get the number 2. The way that we show that that is true is a method of construction. We are going to view this as a constructed object, that as we start from just a point, and we move on, and we put the first edge in, and the second edge in, will see is that this relationship, that the number of vertices we have created up to that point, minus the number of edges, plus the number of regions, is equal to 2, and it will stay 2 as we add an additional edge. This is a wonderful method of proving something in complete generality, because you're proving that during every step of the construction, this feature remains true.

Let's just go ahead and do it. What I'm going to do is I'm going to redraw it with this thicker marker. I'm going to draw on top of it, and we will start with a single point. When I first put the pen on the paper, I had one vertex, and nothing else. Well, let's see what happens. Vertices, 1. Edges, 0. Faces—the whole surrounding region—1; 1+1=2. That's the foundation upon which this entire principle is built.

Now, let's go ahead and put in the first edge. Well, when we put in this first edge, what happens? We put in the first edge, but we also put in the final vertex of that first edge, so we had something where V minus E plus F equals 2. It's actually 1 plus 1 plus 0 equals 2. Well, we added one edge, and we added one additional vertex, so they cancel each other out. The change in the number was nothing. Even though we added one more edge, we also added one more vertex, so the change was nothing.

What happens if we add another edge? Well, look. We go to the next edge. What happens if we add any edge? Well, we're adding one edge plus one vertex. You see? We are always maintaining the property that V minus E plus F equals 2.

Well, let's just continue. We add an edge and add a vertex. Well, we know that as soon as we add an edge, we add a vertex. They cancel out, so we will still get 2. We will still get 2, all the way to here. We will still get 2, all the way to here.

Now, we come to a slightly different situation. Look, right here. You see this edge? Because when we add this edge, we do not add a new vertex, but what do we do? We have already created this arc here, and now we are going to add another edge, so we're going to add an edge, but it's going to an existing vertex, so that means that this vertex was already connected to this vertex, with a connected collection of these arcs, and now we're adding one more edge, but then, we're enclosing something.

We have taken our surrounding space, which up until now, you see, has all been connected. It's all been just one piece, and when we add this edge right here, which I will do right now, we've now made two regions, so that we have added another face at the same time we added another edge, but we did not add another vertex.

Look at these, though. These cancel again. In other words, the new edge is a minus sign, and the new face is a plus sign, and so we maintain the number 2.

Now, we continue. The next edge, again, goes between two existing vertices, so what happens if you make an edge between two existing vertices is that you create another region, because the one region which that edge sat is now divided into two regions. You do not add another vertex, though, because both ends of the new edge are connected to existing vertices. Once again, then, you maintain the number 2.

You see? This is a great insight. Now, look. With the next one, we add an edge and a vertex. Well, we've already analyzed that. If you add an edge and a vertex, you do not change this region. We have not created a new region, because it just sticks out into a region. It does not break it into two pieces. You have another vertex and another edge, then, and they cancel. We still have 2, and look at this. That means that no matter how complicated we get as we go all the way around, we continue to get 2, 2, 2, 2, 2, all the way to the very end.

This insight, this little formula, V minus E plus F equals 2, is called the *Euler characteristic*, named for a mathematician who lived in the 18th century by the name of Euler. The proof that we've just given here is actually known in mathematical circles as a *proof by induction*, because that's what we really did, was to show that the principle we were trying to establish remained true when we did one thing after another, after another, after another, and as long as we kept adding a new edge, it maintained what we had seen to be true.

This is a wonderful insight about any connected doodle that you make in the plane. Now you're asking yourself, though, "Okay, maybe this was moderately interesting, but so what?" In particular, maybe we have forgotten that we are supposed to be talking about the regular solids. What does this have to do with the regular solids?

Let me first of all point something out to you by returning to the chart that we drew up about the regular solids. You see in this chart, where we counted the number of vertices, we counted the number of edges, and we counted the number of faces of each regular solid, and by the way, this may explain the V, the E, and the F in the Euler characteristic, because if you look at the regular solids chart, you will see, if you add up all the numbers for each of the regular solids, look what you get for the tetrahedron: 4 minus 6 plus 4; 4 minus 6 is -2 plus 4 is 2. For the cube: 8 minus 12, -4 plus 6 is 2. Every single row gives you 2.

One thing that we then observe is that the regular solids seem to have the same relationship of the vertices, the edges, and the faces that we had in this Euler characteristic doodle. Still, though, you might say, "Well, wait a minute. There's a problem here," because when I am talking about these edges of a regular solid, I'm not talking about something that's flat on the plane, as I was when I was drawing here on this piece of paper.

The first thing that we have to do, then, is to generalize. This is one of the great strengths of mathematics that once you've done something, you want to say, "Is it true in a more general setting?" This is a wonderful strategy for thinking. If you ever have an idea, then can it apply to a bigger setting? Well, yes it can.

Suppose that we did exactly the same analysis, but instead of doing it on a flat piece of paper, suppose we did it on a balloon, on a sphere, on the boundary of a ball, on the Earth. That is, we drew what we just drew on the sphere. Is there any difference in the analysis that we have here? No. Everything is exactly the same. Therefore, in fact, V minus E plus F equals 2 if you draw on the boundary of a balloon. Okay?

Still, though, you're saying, "How does this connect up to, for example, a cube?" Well, okay. You see this object as a cube, with flat faces, and rigid sides. Let's think a little bit more loosely, though. Let's loosen up a little bit. Suppose you made his cube out of a rubbery substance, and you simply inflated it. You just put a straw in it, and you inflated it, so that it became a sphere, and then, all of these edges became little arcs on the sphere, so that they would have to have the same property of the Euler characteristic being true, V minus E plus F equals 2.

Any solid, any solid, then, in fact, regular or not, has to satisfy the condition V minus E plus F equals 2. Now, that is the insight that we are going to use to prove, once again, that there are only five regular solids. What this really shows, then, is that it's not the fact that the sides are rigid that's essential to knowing that there can be only five. We're going to prove that you couldn't even draw, on a balloon, arcs that made little triangular regions, where there were more than exactly these figures here, that is, where every vertex has the same number of edges coming out, and every region has the same number of edges to it, that these are the only ones you could draw, even if you were drawing with wiggly lines. You see? You have sort of moved from this rigid area into a very amorphous region, and yet, we can still prove something. Let's go ahead and prove it then.

Suppose you have drawn, on a sphere, a drawing that has edges and vertices, and it corresponds to some regular solid. In other words, you imagined that you had a regular solid, and then you expanded it out to a balloon. Okay? Then, every vertex that you have on this balloon expansion of a regular solid would have the same number of edges coming out from it. Right? Because that's a property of being a regular solid. Every region in this blown-up thing has exactly the same number of edges around the region. That's another property of the regular solid. For these, it would be three; for this one, it would be four; and for this one, it would be five.

Then, however, maybe there's one that you can't imagine. Maybe that's seven, or nine, or eleven. Who knows? You see, at this point, we don't know that there are only those five regular solids. Let's give names to these things, then, and here, in the graphic, you'll see what we are going to do: s is going to be the number of sides in each of the regions that we imagine being drawn on this sphere, and c stands for the number of edges that emanate from every vertex. Okay? Therefore, c, in this case, for the cube, is equal to three, because three edges come out from every vertex.

Then, what we are going to do is apply a little bit of analysis. First of all, notice that the number of edges, we can count like we did in the last lecture. How did we count the number of edges? We simply took the number of edges coming out from each vertex, and multiplied them by the number of vertices. That would have given us the number of edges, except that we counted both ends of each edge, so we had to divide by two. This gives a little formula: $E = \dfrac{cV}{2}$; c is the number of things coming out from the corners. Think of c as corner—how many edges come out from each vertex.

Then, you could count the number of vertices by taking the number of faces, multiplying by the number of sides on each face, s. So s times F, and then once again, dividing by c, to get the number of vertices, $V = \dfrac{sF}{c}$, because if you have s sides to each face, and you have F faces, then s times F is the number of vertices. But you have counted them several times, so you have to divide by the number of times that each vertex was counted, which is c.

That gives you the formula $F = \dfrac{cV}{s}$. Now is the time that we use the Euler formula. We know that in this drawing, whatever drawing, remember that you could do it with your eyes closed, has the property that V minus E plus F equals 2. Let's plug in what E and F are, into that formula. We see that V is V minus cV over 2, plus cV over s, is equal to 2, $V = V - \dfrac{cV}{2} + \dfrac{cV}{s} = 2$. You see? Now, if you had this regular solid, it would have to satisfy that condition. Then, we just do a little tiny bit of algebra, and you can see it there on the screen: $2sV - csV + 2cV = 4s$.

We do some algebra, and we see that in order for this to work, it has to have the property that 2 times (s plus c) has to be bigger than c times s, $2(c+s)>cs$. Okay, all you do is plug in those numbers and see what happens. When s, that is, the number of sides in each of the faces is equal to 3, you can choose c to be 3, 4, or 5, and that inequality works. If you try to go too big, though, if you try c equals 6, that is that you have the number of edges coming out from a corner being equal to 6, you get something that would not satisfy this Euler characteristic. You just plug in all the different numbers, and you see that you can't go wrong, that the Euler characteristic is a restriction that tells you that only these five combinations of numbers of edges on each face, and the number of faces, and the number of edges emitting from each vertex, can actually give you a relationship that satisfies this Euler characteristic, if you just dealt with doodles.

This was an interesting way of transporting ourselves out of a particular category of object, namely, rigid things coming into a more amorphous world, making an observation there, and then bringing it back to draw a conclusion about the physical domain in which we began our investigation. That is a typical strategy of scientific investigation and of mathematics.

That was a little bit of technicality. Let me just say a couple of things about these regular solids that are really sort of interesting. I told you that the regular solids had a sort of mystical allure over the millennia, and one person who was really intrigued by them was Kepler. Johannes Kepler was, as you know, the astronomer who lived in about the year 1600, and he was the one who devised the idea that the planets go around in the shape of an ellipse, and other laws of planetary motion. The law that you may not know him for, though, was a law that he was very proud of, and he wrote a book about it. It was called *Mysterium Cosmographicum*.

He was intrigued by the regular solids, and he knew there were five regular solids, and at the time there were six planets that were known. So Kepler found a way to use the regular solids to explain the sizes of the orbits of the planets. He did this by starting with a sphere, putting a regular solid around it, and then circumscribing that with another sphere, and putting another regular solid around it, and so on. In this way he produced six spheres, and by choosing the proper ordering of the regular solids, the radii of the six spheres corresponded pretty well to the sizes of the orbits of the known planets. Now, of course, 150 years later, Uranus was discovered, and yet, we know that there's not going to be another regular solid. This, then, was an example of a theory that was completely bogus, but it was appealing, and showed the allure of the regular solids to Kepler.

I wanted show you one other connection in regard to regular solids with geometry. This is absolutely astounding. If you take an icosahedron, that's the 20-sided figure, and you take any of the edges—here we will balance it on edge, and we will look at one edge here, and you put the straight lines between these edges, here, down to here, and this right here is a rectangle. Do you want to know what kind of a rectangle? A Golden Rectangle. It is exactly the proportions of the Golden Rectangle that you heard about in previous lectures. Look at this, this is a Golden Rectangle, this is a Golden Rectangle, and this is a Golden Rectangle. They fit together in what are called the *Borromean rings*. They won't come apart, and yet, no two of them are linked to each other. That is, then, an amazing convergence of the regular solids with the Golden Rectangle.

I want to finally end up with an idea that is important to you all, which is to explain a soccer ball. If you take a soccer ball, you may say, "Well, what is so interesting about a soccer ball? What does that have to do with the regular solids?" I will tell you what a soccer ball really is. A soccer ball is an icosahedron, a 20-sided figure, where every vertex has been cut off. In other words, this is a blow-up of a vertex. If you cut off the tip of each vertex, you'll end up with hexagonal pieces. Every triangle of this icosahedron becomes a hexagon, and every place where there was a vertex gets cut off, but there were five triangles coming out, so it becomes a pentagon, and sure enough, if you look closely at a soccer ball, they are often colored this way. You'll find that, indeed, there are 20 hexagons and 12 pentagons. It turns out, then, that the regular solids are not only involved in astronomical work, but also involved on the soccer field. Thank you.

Lecture Eleven
Is There a Fourth Dimension? Can We See It?

Edward B. Burger, Ph.D.

Scope:

The very phrase *fourth dimension* conjures up notions of science fiction or, perhaps, the supernatural. The fourth dimension sounds, all at once, eerie, romantic, mysterious, and exciting, and it is. Physicists, artists, musicians, and mystics all visualize the fourth dimension differently and for different purposes. The mystique of the fourth dimension is alluring for all who contemplate it.

Because the fourth dimension lies beyond our daily experience, visualizing, exploring, and understanding it requires us to develop an intuition about a world that we cannot see. Nevertheless, that understanding is within our reach. We will succeed in building insights without experience. We will become at home in an environment that we cannot touch, see, or otherwise sense. An important lesson we will experience here is that explorations of an unfamiliar realm often begin by delving into the depths of the familiar. The fourth dimension provides a dramatic testament to the great power of developing a concept through analogy.

Outline

I. In this lecture, we will attempt an exercise that seems impossible: We will come to understand a universe that we can't perceive.

   A. We'll achieve this understanding through mathematical thinking.

   B. We will use the power of arguing by analogy.

II. What comes to mind when you hear the term *fourth dimension*?

   A. We have all encountered this term before—in science fiction, poetry, and works of art.

   B. Max Weber's *Interior of the Fourth Dimension* conjures up an eerie, foreign world, but by the end of this lecture and the next, you will, hopefully, perceive the fourth dimension as a world that is just over the horizon.

III. We begin by defining the word *dimension*.

    A. *Dimension* is defined by degrees of spatial freedom, that is, how much room we have to move around in our universe. The more room we have, the higher the dimension.

    B. This definition is not particularly rigorous or mathematical. How can we define the term more precisely?

    C. The dimension of a particular universe equates to the number of pieces of information required to isolate any point in that space.

        1. The smallest dimension that we can think of would be a space of zero dimensions. This is the world of a single point. If our world were a single point, we would need no pieces of information to know where we are in that world.

        2. The next higher dimension would be one-dimensional space, or a line. We need only one piece of information to isolate any point on the line.

        3. The next higher dimension would be two-dimensional space, or a plane. Again, we would need two pieces of information to isolate a point on the plane.

        4. We are all familiar with the three-dimensional world, because it is the world of our everyday lives. The surface of this world, which we travel on, may seem two-dimensional, but we still need three pieces of information to isolate any point in this space.

    D. A four-dimensional world would require four pieces of information to isolate a point, but what would be the last piece of information required?

        1. We can't perceive that extra degree of freedom, because we are prisoners of a three-dimensional world.

        2. We will try to understand the concept of the fourth dimension by the process of arguing by analogy.

IV. One way of thinking about the fourth dimension is the "ink-and-drag" method.

    A. If we ink a representation of zero-dimensional space—a marble—and we drag the marble, the result is an increase in dimension to a line.

    B. Similarly, if we ink and drag a line, we produce a two-dimensional space, the plane.

C. If we ink and drag the plane, we create three-dimensional space.

D. Imagine three-dimensional space as a ream of paper. If we ink every point in three-dimensional space and drag it, we achieve four-dimensional space.

V. A different analogy involves stacking points to reach the fourth dimension.

A. If we begin stacking zero-dimensional points, we create a one-dimensional line. By stacking lines, we create the plane, and by stacking planes, we produce three-dimensional space.

B. The ream of paper we saw earlier is an excellent model of this concept. It is a stack of planes of almost zero thickness, yet it fills up space. Looking at the plane of a piece of paper from one direction, it seems to have a good deal of space. Looking at it from the edge, it seems to be almost completely flat.

C. If we can imagine looking at three-dimensional space from a different direction, it too, would look completely flat.

VI. Our difficulty in understanding the fourth dimension is that we cannot perceive it. Let's try to understand the struggles that someone in another dimension would go through in trying to perceive a higher dimension.

A. This exercise captures the essence of a famous book called *Flatland* (1884) by Edwin Abbott.

B. What would a two-dimensional creature look like?

  1. A natural guess might be that the creature would look like a flat drawing of a human.

  2. This guess is incorrect, however. The eyes in such a drawing, for example, would be inside the head and unable to see anything outside that region.

  3. A cutout profile of a head might be a more accurate model of a two-dimensional creature. Notice, too, that as three-dimensional creatures, we have a panoramic view of the two-dimensional head's world and can even see the head's internal organs.

  4. In other words, the two-dimensional world has barriers that, when seen from above in the three-dimensional world, are not really barriers at all.

5. By analogy, a four-dimensional creature would be able to see our internal organs simultaneously with our exterior world.

C. Consider another example of a bar of gold in a safe in a two-dimensional world.
  1. The safe can be opened and the bar of gold can be removed in the two-dimensional world, but in the three-dimensional world, we can steal the gold without opening the safe.
  2. With an extra degree of freedom, a four-dimensional creature could remove a bar of gold from a three-dimensional safe, because the safe would be open to that creature.

D. A lasso in the plane could completely surround a danger in the two-dimensional world.
  1. If a three-dimensional creature lifted up a portion of the lasso, to the two-dimensional creature, that piece of rope would seem to disappear completely.
  2. A closed loop of rope in the three-dimensional world might appear to be magically cut if part of it were picked up by a four-dimensional creature. By analogy, that piece of rope would be dangling in an extra degree of freedom.

VII. We often hear that the fourth dimension may be time.

A. Any attribute can represent dimension, but time is different than space. For example, we can go backwards in space but not in time.

B. We might also think of four dimensions as our three spatial dimensions with the addition of color.

C. If we think of the fourth dimension as time, we can imagine four-dimensional objects as similar to movies or flipbooks.

VIII. We have developed an intuition into the invisible world of the fourth dimension by arguing by analogy. In the next lecture, we'll explore some geometric objects in the fourth dimension.

Suggested Reading:

Edward B. Burger and Michael Starbird, *The Heart of Mathematics: An invitation to effective thinking*, Key College Publishing, Section 4.7, "The Fourth Dimension: Can you see it?"

Questions to Consider:

1. Some four-dimensional person has an object. She shows you just three-dimensional cross-sectional slices of it. The slices look like a circle in one level of four-dimensional space with increasingly smaller circles at each level above and below until they end at a point at the top and a point at the bottom. What is the object?

2. Why could a four-dimensional surgeon remove your appendix without making an incision in your skin?

Lecture Eleven—Transcript
Is There a Fourth Dimension? Can We See It?

Well, today I want us to continue our journey into the visual world of geometry. Now, in the last lecture, Mike was talking about the Platonic solids, and the classical geometry that we have been experiencing all our lives, from the dawn of humanity.

Today, I want us to think about a world that we actually can't see, and yet, we can consider the visual aspects of it just the same, and that is the world of the *fourth dimension*.

You know, it was Johannes Kepler and who once wrote: "If there is anything that can bind the heavenly mind of man to this dreary exile of our earthly home and can reconcile us with our fate so that one can enjoy living—then it is verily the enjoyment of the mathematical sciences…"

I think that quote is so apt to this lecture, because in this lecture, we're going to do something that seems, at first, to be impossible. We are going to wrap our minds around a universe that we can't perceive, and we're going to do that through mathematical thinking.

How can mathematical thinking, then, allow us to wrap our minds around things that we can't even imagine at first? Well, the answer is twofold. Number one, we're going to see the power of using the strategy of arguing by analogy, the idea that if something is too difficult, we should admit it, confess it, celebrate it, and not look at it anymore, because it is too hard. Instead, let's look at a simpler circumstance, an easier question, and build insight, intuition, and through that development, all of a sudden, by analogy, we can build understanding into the abstract realm that seemed impenetrable.

Now, when you think of the fourth dimension, what comes to mind? Well, all sorts of things, because we hear that phrase, "the fourth dimension," all the time. We hear it in science fiction, we hear it in poetry, in drama, and so forth. What is it? What can we see? In fact, many artists have tried to capture the fourth dimension. In fact, here, we can see a work of Max Weber's, *Interior of the Fourth Dimension*, and we see that in this image, it sort of conjures up an eerie, foreign world.

Well, my hope is that by the end of this lecture and the end of the next lecture, you will come to see the fourth dimension not as an eerie, foreign world, but as a world that is just over the horizon for us to enjoy, and yet, we can still think about it and appreciate it today.

Okay, so, how can we wrap our minds around the fourth dimension? Well, what really begs to be asked here is: What is the fourth dimension? Or, even more simply, if we are going to understand simple things deeply, what does the word "dimension" even mean? Well, that's where we are going to start. We're going to figure out exactly what we mean by "dimension," and then from there, start to build, and see if we can understand what the fourth dimension is.

Well, when I think of the word "dimension," what I think of are degrees of spatial freedom. How much room do we have to move around in our universe? The more room we have, the more roomy it is, then, in fact, I would say, the bigger the dimension. If we are confined and restricted in some way, then, I would say the dimension would be a little bit smaller.

That is, then, a sort of humanistic interpretation of "dimension," but not particularly rigorous or mathematical. How, then, can we give a mathematical notion to what "dimension" means? Let's try to make it very concrete.

I will say that the dimension of a particular universe is simply the number of pieces of information that are required in order to isolate and pick out any particular point. Any particular point in the space. How many pieces of information do you have to tell me in order for me to find any point? Let's look at some examples.

For example, what's the smallest dimension you can think of? Well, you might say, "Gee, the smallest dimension I can think of is one dimension. That seems pretty small." However, you are far, far from where you could be, because of course, the smallest dimension that I can think of is zero dimensions. Zero dimensions, and so, what would that world look like? Well, that world would just be a point. It would just be a dot. Now, I actually have an artist's rendition of a zero-dimensional space, so it would just be a point. This would be it.

Now, the reason I say it is an artist's rendition is because if you look at this, the fact that you can physically see this is because it actually has thickness. It is actually a huge black marble, so that it actually has thickness, and volume, and so forth. It is not really a dot, but it conjures up the idea of a dot. If you really want to see zero-dimensional space, I can show you that. For zero-dimensional space, in fact, all you have to do is take a pushpin, and if you take a pushpin and look at the dangerous end, at the very tip, that very sharp point, that point right above it is zero-dimensional space. That's how small it is. In fact, then, if you put your finger there, ow!—it hurts, so no one said that zero-dimensional space is necessarily friendly, because it's sort of sharp, but you can feel it, and you can sort of see that that end of the pin is pointing to zero. That is how small it is. It really is zero.

I will use this, though, quite often in the next two lectures to conjure up this notion, since I'm afraid I'm going to potentially do some damage to my fingers, so we'll see this not too often, but this will capture the idea of zero-dimensional space.

Now, why is it zero-dimensional space? Well, it is zero-dimensional space, because if this were all we had, if that were all there was, I would not have to give you any directions to tell you where I am. Everything is here. There's just one point. Basically, then, if we were all in zero-dimensional space, we would all be home by now, because everything is there. It would just be one big party. Everyone would be there, and there would be no place to move, so in fact, zero pieces of information are required in order to know where I am in a zero-dimensional world.

Now, what would be the next dimension up? Well, you might guess one-dimensional space. Well, why is one-dimensional space, in fact, one-dimensional? Well, if you think of one-dimensional space, you might visualize it as a line. Well, okay. If you think of this as a numbered line—so imagine numbers here, 0, 1, 2, 3, 4, and so forth—then, to isolate any particular point on that line, all I have to do is give you the number. Like 6. Then, you know, 1, 2, 3, 4, 5, 6. "Oh, Ed is right here," and there I would be.

If you wish, you can think of it like a street. There's one infinitely long street, and all you have to do is give me your street address. One piece of information. Some people might say, "Gee, if it's just the number of directions, shouldn't it be two, because we can go this way or that way." Well, that's one way of thinking about directions, but in these lectures, we're going to think about dimension as the minimum of pieces of information required. In this case, even though we can move back and forth, it's only in this one linear fashion that we can do so, so one piece of information is required.

What would be the next dimension up? Well, the next dimension up that you might think of would be like a flat surface, like a plane, in fact, like the plane here on this easel. Because here, notice that if you were to think about it, two pieces of information would be required. In a way, you cannot imagine having axes drawn, if you wanted to think about it, and you would not only have to give me the street address, but you would have to tell me what street you were on, so that you have to say, "Go up five, and then over three," and that would locate a point precisely.

In fact, then, here on the plane, on the surface of this black fabric, what we see is that in fact, two pieces of information are necessary in order to locate any particular point on the plane, how far over and how far up, and so therefore, this has two dimensions.

What about a three-dimensional world? Well, a three-dimensional world, in fact, is something very familiar to us, because it is all around us. That's the world that we live in in our everyday lives. Is it really three dimensions? It sure is, and let me show you why. If I pick a point that I can sort of think of as the center point—let's, for example, think of the very corner of this desk right here as the center of our entire universe; that's a little bit egotistical, since I'm so close to it, but what the heck. That's the center, so I predict that every single point that you can possibly think of and point to can be given by just three pieces of information emanating from here.

For example, suppose my nose. How would you tell me where my nose is? Well, I would say, you would go over in this direction this much, you would come out this direction this much, and then you would go up right to here. That would locate my nose. Thus, three pieces of information are required. Therefore, we can think of going in this direction, that's one dimension; in this direction, that's another dimension; and then up and down. In fact, you might say, "Gee, this doesn't sound quite right, because I know that when I'm going to visit a friend's house, they just tell me what street they're on, and they tell me their number. It seems like that might be two dimensions."

Well, if you think about it, it is actually still three dimensions, because if someone says to you, "I live at 105 Main Street," then, if you go to 105 Main Street, you get to a building, but where in the building is that person? You would have to know the height. Is he or she in the basement? Is he or she on the first floor, the second floor, the third floor, and so forth? In fact, really, then, we're living in a three-dimensional world, although the surface that we travel on, of course, is a plane, but we still need to know the height. Is he or she in the penthouse, as he or she would love to be, or maybe a little bit lower? Three dimensions, then, describe our world.

What is a four-dimensional world, then? A four-dimensional world, in fact, would be one where we would have four different degrees of freedom. That is, we need four pieces of information in order to isolate any particular point and locate it. Where would I point to that extra direction, though? We already have one direction going this way, one direction going this way, and then one direction going this way. So no matter where I point, I'm staying within the realm of those three. Well, the problem is that we can't perceive that extra degree of freedom, because, in fact, we're creatures, prisoners, if you will, of three dimensions. It is going to be difficult, then, for us to wrap our minds around a four-dimensional world, since we can't see it, and thus, the problem. The problem is: How can we make sense out of a world that is actually beyond our grasp?

Well, the way we are going to do that is to argue by analogy, and this is not only so important in understanding higher dimensions, but it is also so important in understanding so many issues that arise in our everyday lives, and as a great strategy of thinking—remember this course is *The Joy of Thinking*—one of the great strategies, in fact, is arguing by analogy: Looking at simple cases very, very deeply.

Let's try to build up a little bit of momentum to get to the fourth dimension. One way of thinking about it, for example, is to use a method that I refer to as the "ink-and-drag" method. Let me quickly show you the "ink-and-drag" method. Here I have a little inkpad. It is a standard inkpad, that we use all the time for stamps. Well, imagine that this inkpad has some very special properties, so that not only when you dip something onto it can you make an imprint, but imagine that when you put this special ink on an object, if you were just to drag it, there would actually be a residue that would remain, almost like a star sort of shifting by, and you could actually see the ink remaining, as you scanned it over. Then, you could actually use this to build higher dimensions. Let me show you.

We start with zero-dimensional space, remember that this is just a model—zero-dimensional space is really just a dot—and I put it on this inkpad, so I ink it up, and now, I'm going to drag it in a new direction, and if I do that, can you see what's going to be swept out? What's actually going to be swept out, is, in fact, this line, so we can think of the line as a "swept-out point," if you will. Now, remember, this is just an artist's rendition of a line. A line is really invisible, since it is just a swept-out version of an invisible point, but again, this is just an artist's rendition.

Now, what if we were to take the entire line and put it on the inkpad, and now, sweep it out in a new direction? Well, if I sweep it out in a new direction, you can see that I'm beginning to produce what would look like space. You can see that this black board here, in fact, can be thought of as a swept-out version of the black line.

Okay, well, now, we're making great progress, because what would you do next? Well, if you wanted to, you could take the blackboard, and you could literally ink up the whole blackboard on the pad, and now, sweep it out in a new direction, and if I were to come up, you see, like this, I would be sweeping out space. I would be sweeping out space. Therefore, if you wanted to see a model of space, for example, I happen to have a model of space right here. Here's a model of space. Heavy.

Now, let's argue by analogy. If we wanted to now build the fourth dimension, what would we do? Well, it doesn't seem to make a lot of sense, but let's just say it anyway. What we would do is we would take all of space, and we would ink it up, so it's sort of peculiar. We would take every single molecule, not just the boundary here, but every molecule, as we did with the plane. We ink up every single point, and then we take them and drag them in a different direction, so I take this and I literally—I can't do this physically, but you have to now pretend that I'm doing this—I'm dragging it in a new direction. I'm certainly dragging it, but now imagine that I am dragging it in a different direction. That swept-out thing that I'm making, the residue that the ink is leaving behind, in fact, is a model of four-dimensional space, so that it is this action that you are watching me do right now that is trying to capture the idea of four-dimensional space. Still, in my mind, it is a little hard to see.

Let's try it a different way, then. If we try a different way, can think of it as sort of on the microlevel, if you wanted to, and instead of thinking about it as inking up and dragging, we can think about it as a stacking process, stacking points. Suppose that we just start with a point. I will put a point right here, and now, what I am going to do is take lots of points. Now remember, think of that as being zero, really, not a thick ball. Now, if I take lots of points, and start to put it on, what happens? Well, what happens is that they start to produce this length, and they start to sweep out, you can see, what appears to be the line. By just stacking the points, then, we are producing a line.

By stacking the line, you can now see, again arguing by analogy, that we're going to be producing the plane. By stacking the planes, one on top of each other, what we produce, in fact, is this three-dimensional cube of space.

Now, in fact, this is very accurate, and I want us to take a look at this for a second, because you see that this is filling up space, a little brick of space, but each sheet of the two-dimensional universe here, you will notice has no thickness at all. No thickness at all. Of course, this paper really does have thickness, but in the ideal setting, this would have no thickness. Yet, when I am sort of stacking them on top of each other, they start to sweep out this extra direction, so when you hear people talk about parallel universes, in fact, this is what they mean, the idea that this could be a whole two-dimensional universe, and right next to it could be another two-dimensional universe, and in fact, they're right next to each other, but they are parallel and different, and yet, they fill out space.

The idea of stacking, then, and the idea that even though this has lots of space this way, in a new direction, a direction that we can't perceive, this way or this way, but in this direction, there in fact is no thickness at all. Space, then, is flat if you look at it in a new direction.

What about three-dimensional space? Arguing by analogy, we see the same thing. We see that if we could look at our space, which seems to be all around us, in a new direction, how would it appear? Well, if you argue by analogy, you see that it would appear completely flat. It would be flat, which seems so counterintuitive, because you know that it would be a piece of paper then, but the point is that in a new direction that I can't point to, we, all this space, would look just as flat as the piece of paper looks when you view it in this new direction, like this.

In fact, we can think of three-dimensional space (if we allow ourselves to think in the fourth dimension) as flat, and we can now imagine taking various copies of three-dimensional space and stacking them one on top of the other, to sweep out a four-dimensional world.

Well, again, pretty difficult to fathom, and for good reason, because we can't see that extra degree of freedom. When we're really stuck, then, what we should really do is to retreat and go back to an easier question. The difficulty here is that we cannot fathom the fourth dimension because we cannot perceive it. Let's try to understand and appreciate the struggles that someone will go through when he or she cannot see a dimension, and he or she is trying to understand it, but in a realm where we ourselves know what things look like.

In particular, I want to sort of capture the essence of a very famous book by Edwin Abbott called *Flatland*, which he wrote in 1884. He wasn't actually a mathematician; he was a theologian, but he was enamored with this idea of flatlands. It's a very, very tiny book, and it's a beautiful read, and it really tries to capture the idea of the fourth dimension, and he does it by analogy. When he does this, instead of trying to have us try to wrap our minds around four dimensions, as three-dimensional creatures, how about a world of two dimensions? A world of two dimensions, and we try to explain to two-dimensional creatures what, in fact, a three-dimensional world is.

The first question is: What would I look like if I were a two-dimensional creature? Suppose that I lived on the surface of this easel. What would I look like? Well, a natural guess might be this. Here's an artist's rendition of me, maybe. I might think that's me. I am sort of skinny-looking, right? Glasses and so forth? Right, but that's actually not a good guess, and the reason is because if my entire universe was, in fact, the surface of this easel, let's look at my eyes for a second. What would I be able to see in my world? Well, look really closely, and you'll see that my eye would be able to look out and see the inside of my glasses, and if I looked out here, I could see the inside of these glasses here, and here, and here. I couldn't see outside my glasses. In fact, my eyebrow would even block my field of vision.

Similarly, here, my eyeballs, when they would look out into the universe, which is just here, would just see the inside of my glasses. This, in fact, is not how I would look as a two-dimensional creature. Notice that my mouth, for example, is on the inside of my head, so that if there were food here, if there were a piece of food, and I wanted to get to it, that food could not get to me, because it would keep hitting the side of my face. I couldn't get it in. Where are our mouths? Our mouths are not on the insides of our bodies, but are on the interface between the exterior and the interior world, so that we can put things in. Similarly, my mouth should not be inside, but should be on the outside.

A better version of how I might look might be something like this. This might more clearly capture the idea of what a two-dimensional creature would look like. Notice that my eye can see out into my world. Remember that my world is just this black surface here. My mouth is here, so I can actually put food in, which is really good, but notice something else interesting. From your vantage point, you have a panoramic view of the second dimension that we as two-dimensional creatures can't appreciate, because you can see it all at once; it's a panoramic view. All I can see is straight ahead, so in particular, you can actually see my brain. You can actually see the inside of my body, even though, of course, if I had a friend here, if my friend would look at me, what would my friend see? All my friend would see when he looked out with those two-dimensional eyes would be just my skin, which is this one-dimensional feature right here, and if he looks all around me, I'm completely sealed up to him. I'm completely sealed to him, even though from your extra degree of freedom, you can actually see inside and outside at the same time.

Again, it's a peculiar thing to explain. If you wanted to give me a lobotomy, for example—it might not be a bad idea—you wouldn't even have to cut my one-dimensional skin open, because all you would have to do is literally just go there and start touching my brain, without even cutting my skin.

Similarly, arguing by analogy, if there were a four-dimensional creature, how would we look? Well, we would look open to that creature. That creature would be able to see our internal organs simultaneously with our exterior world. We would be opened up, just as I'm opened here as a two-dimensional creature. Are we really sort of cut open? No, it is that extra degree of freedom that allows a four-dimensional creature to peer right in.

Let me try to illustrate this with some quick examples. For example, suppose that I had some gold here that I wanted to protect, so here I am, protecting my gold. You can see that it's kept in a two-dimensional vault, which is good, because that's my world. I will have my friend here also guard it, so we are all watching the sides. If I wanted to get to the gold, by the way, what I would have to do is actually open the vault, and then remove the gold. Okay, fine. I'm going to seal the vault, though, and I'm going to watch around here, my friend is going to watch around here, and it's completely covered and guarded.

Now, as three-dimensional creatures, though, I claim that we can actually steal the gold without ever breaking the vault. How can we do that? Well, now I'll be a three-dimensional creature. All you do is come right over, parallel to the whole universe, and just take out the gold. Notice that I never actually touched the vault. Well, what happens when I, as a two-dimensional creature, open the vault? When I open the vault, what do I see? It's gone. I'm all excited. It disappeared. How could that be? I don't understand it, because my friend and I were watching the whole time, and no one ever even came by, and yet, now, it's gone. How can that be explained?

Well, the idea is that we came in from an extra degree of freedom. What would the analogy be here? The analogy might be something like this. Imagine that you have something in a sealed box. You take a sealed box, and you open it up, and you put something inside of it, like the gold, and you close it. Now, from our vantage point, we can watch all the sides, all the sides very carefully, and guard it, and no one is ever coming in, but if there's a four-dimensional creature, this box would be open, just like this is open to us. That person could reach in, grab it, and we would open it up, and what would we see? It's empty. It's empty, and what a sort of eerie feeling. It's almost like magic, but really, it makes complete sense if we view that extra degree of freedom as a thing we can go through and pierce.

Let me show you another quick example, just to build some more intuition. Let's assume that, in fact, there was a two-dimensional killer bee that was in the two-dimensional world—that a former student sent it to me as a gift—and that it could kill just by touching you. However, happily, there's a red lasso around it, so therefore, in fact, I'm protected. Well, how could someone actually have this killer bee provide some terrorism upon me? Well, they couldn't touch the bee, because then they would be dead, but what could they do with the rope? If it were a three-dimensional person, a three-dimensional student, they could actually pick up a piece of the rope, and what would happen if the rope were to be picked up out of the plane of the universe?

Now, let's think about it from the vantage point of two-dimensional me, so here is the plane. You see that my eye is right along the plane, and I see that rope. What would happen if the rope were to be lifted up? Now, if it were to be lifted up, of course, it would just be coming over here, but all I can see is that line of sight. What would happen to the rope? It would just disappear, because part of it would be hanging out in the extra dimension, so all of a sudden, the extra rope just disappears. Oh, my goodness, and what is looking at me is this terrorist bee that can come and attack me. Just by lifting up the rope, the rope would disappear, and then, when the bee escaped, what could my three-dimensional student do? That three-dimensional student could just let the rope go back into my world, and what would the illusion be? The rope would just fuse back together, so that what I would see my universe of two dimensions is that the rope would disappear, and then glue back together, even though what was actually happening was that it was dangling with an extra degree of freedom.

How can we actually show this in our world? Here, I've got some scissors, and here, I've got a loop of rope with a knot in it, and it's a sealed rope, you can see. What can I do? Well, without ever cutting it—I'm going to leave the scissors right here, so that you can see I am never, ever going to cut it—I'm going to use the fourth dimension. I'm going to take a piece of this rope and push it into the fourth dimension. If I push it into the fourth dimension, what is the illusion that we would see? It would look like the rope would actually be broken open, but really, it's not broken. It's just hanging in an extra degree of freedom, just like this rope was pulled out, and off the plane. If we do that, then, what we would see is something like this.

Now, it looks like I broke the rope, but I didn't, because the scissors are way over there. I never touched the scissors. What really is happening here, then, what we can think of is that that rope is still connecting this end to that end, but in an extra degree of freedom, just like when I lifted this up. It looked broken to the two-dimensional creature, but really was just hanging in an extra dimension. Well, now that it is open in our world, we can certainly untangle it, and so if we untangle it, it's pretty easy to undo the knot, and then, if it let that four-dimensional creature drop that loop back into our world, just like we dropped back the loop into the plane, and it sealed itself up, we do that here, and it seals itself up. There it is, sealed up completely. Using the fourth dimension, you can even undo knots. That's a handy little trick to remember if you ever get into a knotty situation.

Anyway, the point is that we can now argue by analogy, and begin to see four dimensions as sort of a stacked-up version of three-dimensional space, and you can argue by these analogies to see how one might perceive certain activities transpiring in the fourth dimension.

Now, a lot of times in science fiction, or maybe just in literature, you read the question of: Is the fourth-dimension time? Well, maybe it is, and the truth is that you can have any attribute represent dimension. In fact, if you think about our lives as sort of a long sequence of events, if you just kind of follow your life, if you left a residue, and inked yourself up, and walked through life leaving this complicated residue of where you were going, that can be thought of as a four-dimensional thing, because once time is going, you see, any instant and the next instant are sort of parallel universes, three-dimensional spaces that are one second apart.

You can think that way, and that's fine. People can do that, and people do do that. In terms of time, though, it's a little bit difficult, because it's different than space. For example, I don't how to go backward in time, whereas I can easily go backward in space, so that, in fact, if we are thinking about the fourth dimension as a spatial object, it doesn't seem particularly fair that somehow that fourth, that new extra dimension to us, in fact, is going to be something so foreign and different.

For example, we could have viewed the third dimension in a two-dimensional world as time. We can do that as well. We can then think of three dimensions as a two-dimensional planar world with the addition of time. That's another model for three dimensions, but it isn't one that is sort of spatial and familiar to us in our everyday world.

In fact, any attribute can be thought of as a dimension, so that in fact, you can think of the fourth dimension, if you will, as our three spatial dimensions with the addition of color. So that I say, "Go over this much, go up this much, come over, there's a point, and now think 'chartreuse.'" Whereas if I say, "Now think 'yellow,'" it's a different point in four-dimensional space. Any attribute that you can think of at this point—sound; you can sit here and think of "C sharp" or "A flat," and those are also different points in a four-dimensional space. Any attribute, again, can, in fact, be used to capture this.

In fact, if you think of the fourth dimension as time, you can sort of see interesting things. For example, I can actually think of three-dimensional objects, if you will, as movies. In fact, if you remember when I had that big stack of paper, and I was moving it back and forth, and I said, "It's actually the action of moving that stack of paper that's producing the fourth dimension," it sort of was that movie, and you can sort of think of at like a flip book, if you will, and you can pretend that that flip book motion picture is capturing the fourth dimension, in a sense, through time.

For example, I can show you a visual of what a fourth-dimensional sphere might look like by a little flip book. Now, if you think about what a sphere is, you can imagine taking a sphere and moving it through a two-dimensional world. What would you first see? This sphere would first just touch the world at a point. Then, as the sphere passed through the world, we would see little circles that would become big circles, until we got to the largest banded part of the circle, and then, it would shrink back down to a dot.

What would happen if we took a four-dimensional sphere and moved it through our world? Well, arguing by analogy, we would see a dot, and then, a bigger sphere, and then a bigger sphere, and so forth.

Let me show you this now. I'm actually going to show you what this flipbook looks like. I hope you can see it. I want you to look really, really closely. I will do it a couple of times, and you can see that it's a little motion picture, and that little motion picture is showing a sphere going from a dot to a big sphere, back to a little dot again, and that's what the illusion would be if we took a sphere and moved it through, so there you have it.

Well, it turns out that we can develop an intuition into worlds that are invisible, just by arguing by analogy and looking at simple things deeply. Now, while the fourth dimension still remains invisible to us, in the next lecture, we're going to attempt to actually make it more visible to our eyes, at least to our mind's eye, by exploring some

©2003 The Teaching Company

geometric objects in the fourth dimension. We are actually going to build some physical objects that are going to capture or resemble, in some unusual way, what four-dimensional objects look like, so get ready for that adventure in the next lecture.

Lecture Twelve
The Invisible Art of the Fourth Dimension

Edward B. Burger, Ph.D.

Scope:

To further illustrate the notion of spatial degrees of freedom and dimensionality, we now consider the geometry of the fourth dimension. We will begin with a look at artistic works inspired by dimension, such as Duchamp's *Nude Descending a Staircase #2* (1912). We then create our own artistic work by building and visualizing a four-dimensional cube. We will proceed, as always, by beginning with the familiar and moving on from there. This method will allow us to construct cubes in successively higher dimensions using the cubes constructed in the previous dimensions. After constructing a four-dimensional cube, we can unfold its boundary just as we can unfold the boundary of an ordinary cube. The unfolded four-dimensional cube is a further source of artistic inspiration, as we see, for example, in Dali's *Crucifixion (Corpus Hypercubicus).*

Outline

I. In this lecture, we return to the fourth dimension. In particular, we'll explore the geometry of the fourth dimension.

   A. Artists have tried to capture the essence of the fourth dimension on canvas.

   1. As we saw in the last lecture, Max Weber created an eerie image of it in *Interior of the Fourth Dimension.*

   2. Marcel Duchamp's *Nude Descending a Staircase #2* shows the totality of motion as a figure moves down a staircase, rather than a snapshot of one moment in time.

   B. In this lecture, we will try to construct our own work of art— a four-dimensional cube. How can we accomplish this when we can't even see the fourth dimension? As before, we will argue by analogy and try to understand simple things deeply.

II. We begin the construction process in the smallest dimension we can think of—zero dimension.

   A. In zero-dimensional space, everything is the point; thus, a zero-dimensional cube is the point.

B. To move up a dimension, we ink the point and drag it in a new direction. The result, of course, is a line segment, or a one-dimensional cube.

C. Repeating the process, we ink the line segment and drag it in a perpendicular direction for a two-dimensional cube.

D. For a three-dimensional cube, we ink the two-dimensional version and drag it in a new perpendicular direction.

E. For a four-dimensional cube, we would have to ink every point in the cube—not just its surface, but every point inside the cube. Think of the cube as a sponge that is completely saturated with ink.

    1. Moving the three-dimensional cube in a new perpendicular direction is a problem, because we can't point to a direction that is simultaneously perpendicular to the three that we're accustomed to.

    2. We can abstract the dragging motion, however, and construct a model of the result.

III. Our model seems complicated in comparison with a three-dimensional cube. Let's look more deeply at the three-dimensional cube to try to understand the four-dimensional version.

A. First, we look at some two-dimensional perspective drawings of the three-dimensional cube.

    1. If we read these drawings literally, we see that they are not accurate representations of a cube. That is, the sides are not of equal length, the angles are not equal, and so on.

    2. We have the ability, however, to visualize the three-dimensional object from the two-dimensional picture.

B. Our model of the four-dimensional cube is the three-dimensional equivalent of the two-dimensional drawing. If the model were in four-dimensional space, every side would be the same length, every angle would be 90 degrees, and so on.

C. Of course, we can continue the earlier process of inking and dragging to produce a five-dimensional cube with the four-dimensional version.

D. Once we have these models of cubes in higher dimensions, we can begin to examine them for patterns.

  1. For example, we can count the vertices of the cubes in each dimension: A zero-dimensional cube (a point) has 1 vertex, a one-dimensional cube (a line) has 2 vertices, a two-dimensional cube (a square) has 4 vertices, and a three-dimensional cube has 8 vertices.

  2. We can see that the pattern is to double the number of vertices of the cube in the lower dimension to find the number of vertices in the next dimension. Thus, a four-dimensional cube will have 16 vertices, and a five-dimensional cube will have 32 vertices.

  3. The same process can be repeated to determine the number of edges in the four-dimensional cube. In this case, we begin with the lower-dimensional cube, then double the number of its edges and add the number of its vertices.

IV. As we saw earlier, our model of a four-dimensional cube is flawed because not all the sides are the same length, not all the angles are 90 degrees, and so on. How can we build a closer approximation?

  A. Again, let's begin with a simpler case—the three-dimensional cube. How can we capture a perfect three-dimensional cube—with all 90-degree angles and all side lengths the same—in a two-dimensional drawing?

  B. The trick, of course, is to unfold the cube and lay it flat. To reconstruct the cube, we would have to use the extra degree of freedom offered by three-dimensional space.

  C. We can mark all the edges of the two-dimensional cube to show how they could be reconnected to form a three-dimensional cube.

  D. Can we unfold a four-dimensional cube in a similar fashion? What are the boundaries of a four-dimensional cube?

  1. Again, arguing by analogy, the boundaries of a one-dimensional cube were the zero-dimensional points. The boundaries of a two-dimensional cube were the one-dimensional line segments. The boundaries of a three-dimensional cube are the two-dimensional faces of the square. Thus, the boundaries of a four-dimensional cube are three-dimensional cubes.

2. We can count all the three-dimensional cubes that form the boundaries of the model of the four-dimensional cube. We find eight cube-shaped faces in the four-dimensional cube.

3. If we were to unfold the four-dimensional cube, it would resemble a three-dimensional crucifix.

E. This unfolded four-dimensional cube was the inspiration for *Crucifixion* (*Corpus Hypercubicus*) by Salvador Dali.

V. Let's close with just one more construction project—a tetrahedron.

A. A tetrahedron is similar to a pyramid, but every face is a triangle.

B. We start with a zero-dimensional tetrahedron, a point. To build a one-dimensional tetrahedron, we take a copy of the original point and connect the two.

C. To form a two-dimensional tetrahedron, or a triangle, we take another copy of the point and connect it to the previous points.

D. For a three-dimensional tetrahedron, we add another point and connect it to the previous points, or *cone* it over each of the vertices. The result is the tetrahedron, or a pyramid shape.

E. For a four-dimensional tetrahedron, we simply add another point in four-dimensional space and connect it to all the previous points.

E. As we have seen, this exercise allows us to expand our intuition by looking at simple things deeply.

Suggested Reading:

Edward B. Burger and Michael Starbird, *The Heart of Mathematics: An invitation to effective thinking*, Key College Publishing, Section 4.7, "The Fourth Dimension: Can you see it?"

Questions to Consider:

1. Produce edge drawings of the regular cube, the four-dimensional cube, the five-dimensional cube, and the six-dimensional cube.

2. We saw how to build cubes in all dimensions, and saw a little about how to build higher dimensional tetrahedra. A zero-dimension triangle is just a point. A one-dimensional triangle is a line segment; a two-dimensional tetrahedron is a triangle; you know what a three-dimensional tetrahedron is. What is the pattern? We add a point in the next dimension and join all points you had before to this new point with edges. Sketch a four-dimensional triangle and then a five-dimensional triangle. Fill in the following table:

Dimension of the triangle	Number of vertices	Number of edges	Number of 2-dim faces	Number of 3-dim "faces"
1				
2				
3				
4				
5				
n (in general)				

Lecture Twelve—Transcript
The Invisible Art of the Fourth Dimension

In our last lecture, we began to wrap our minds around a world that is completely invisible, and at the moment, foreign to us, the world of the fourth dimension. Trying to understand that world is a wonderful illustration of looking for patterns by arguing by analogy. By looking at simple things deeply, all of a sudden hidden and often invisible structure comes into focus, and that it really is sort of the meta life lesson and the meta mathematical thinking lesson for both the last lecture, and continuing on into this lecture, where we are going to explore the fourth dimension in even greater detail.

In particular, I want us, in this lecture, to think about the actual geometry of the fourth dimension, even though the fourth dimension remains something that we can't even see.

e.e. cummings once wrote: "listen, there's a helluva universe next door, let's go." That really captures the spirit of what I think of when I think of the fourth dimension, especially if you really do remember from the last lecture, where we can think of increasing dimensions by looking at slices of space, or taking spaces and stacking one on top of the other to build larger spaces. Really, then, "next door," the fourth dimension is waiting for us.

Now, many people have tried to capture the fourth dimension through literature, and even through art. In fact, if we take a look at some images, we can now return to Max Weber's work, *Interior of the Fourth Dimension*, which we saw in the last lecture, and we see that sort of eerie and foreign world, that seems scary and cold. But there are other images, too. For example, if you look at Marcel Duchamp's *Nude Descending a Staircase #2*, this is a wonderful image, because here, what we see is the idea of looking at the totality of motion.

Remember, thinking about the fourth dimension as perhaps time, or that trail, if you remember from the last lecture, where if we actually inked ourselves up, and then walked through our lives and left a trail, that is what is captured in this image. As the figure is descending the staircase, what we get is not just a frozen moment in time, but, in fact, the totality of motion, and thus, capturing the fourth dimension. Again, once we think of mathematics, and embrace it, we can even appreciate the arts in a richer and more detailed way.

Today, though, what I want us to do is not to look at other people's works of art, but instead to actually produce our own, and I want us, in fact, to try to build a four-dimensional cube. Now, how in the world can we build a four-dimensional cube when we can't even see the fourth dimension? Answer: We learned it last time. It is to argue by analogy, and to understand simple things deeply. Let's look so closely at things that are so familiar that we just take them for granted, but by focusing on that structure, by looking at it really closely, all of a sudden, we begin to see insights and develop ideas that will naturally just guide us to the fourth dimension. Let's begin.

Well, where would you begin to build a four-dimensional cube? If we were going to look at something a little bit easier, you might say, "Ed, why don't we look at a three-dimensional cube?" But that would be far, far, far too complicated. We always start at the beginning, so what's the smallest dimension that we can think of? From the last lecture, we saw that it was, in fact, zero dimensions. You may remember, in fact, that the zero dimension is just a point, and literally, this is just an artist's rendition. In today's lecture, you're going to see lots of pieces of art, and we have to understand that all of those are artists' renditions of the actual reality. Remember, the reality is that zero-dimensional space is what this pin is pointing to, the very end of that, and just above it. That really is zero. That point, in fact, captures what a zero-dimensional space would be, or a point. For our vision today, though, so that we can actually see it, we're going to embrace this as a point, as a model for the point.

Okay, what is a zero-dimensional cube? Answer: The point. Because remember, everything is the point, so zero-dimensional space is so easy. If we ever had to take a test on zero-dimensional space, everyone would get a perfect score, because the answer is always "a point."

All right, but let's quickly move from here to the next type of cube. Let's ask: What, in fact, is a one-dimensional cube? How can we build it? Well, we've already seen the strategy in the last lecture. What I'm going to do is to take the zero-dimensional cube, also known as a point, and then I am going to now ink it up on that sort of mathematical, magical inkpad that we had, which leaves a trail, a residue. I ink it up, and what I am going to do is actually drag it straight for one unit in a new direction, and when I do that, you can see that I am actually going to sweep out a line segment, and in fact, the line segment is precisely a one-dimensional cube, also known as a line segment, but that now produces the one-dimensional cube.

Okay, well, now, we're certainly on a roll here. What do I do now? I take the one-dimensional cube, and do what to it? I'm just going to now repeat the process that we've established. I am going to take the one-dimensional cube, put it on this inkpad, and I'm going to get it all inky, so here we go, it's all inked up, and now, I am going to drag it in a different direction. Now, notice that if I were to take it, and drag it in this direction, that's not a new direction, so that I would just be making my one-dimensional cube, or in this case, a line segment that's just longer.

What I really want to do is ink it up, and move it in a different direction. Since I'm trying to build a cube, what I want to do is to move it in a direction that's perpendicular to the direction that I currently have, so now I have to do it, and watch what happens. I sweep out, and if you watch carefully, you can see what I am sweeping out. You can see that I'm sweeping out a perfect square, so that in fact, by sweeping this out, we produce the square, and you can actually see the sweeping take place, to give rise to the square. Now, we have the one-dimensional cube, which gives rise to the two-dimensional cube, which is more familiarly known to us as the square.

Now, how do I go from the square to the three-dimensional cube? Well, the three-dimensional cube, of course, we know, and I can actually draw a picture of a three-dimensional cube. Let me do that. I want to actually impress upon you my artistic abilities, so here we go.

Now, if you want to draw a three-dimensional cube—by the way, I promise you that I can actually draw it a lot better than I am going to, but I'm drawing it this way for a very particular reason, and you'll see why in a moment. Here's one version of it. Let me just show you that in midstream. There's one version of the cube. Not bad, huh? That's sort of impressive. Not bad, and it captures what a three-dimensional cube looks like. Let me show you a three-dimensional cube from a different vantage point just for fun, since I'm getting interested in and involved in this. Now, drawing cubes is kind of like potato chips. You just can't do one. You know, once you have one, you say, "You know, just one more, and then maybe I will be satisfied," and sometimes you are, and sometimes you have to draw more, but for the purposes of this lecture, I will curb that temptation and just draw you that one. That's a version of the cube where you look right inside the top, and you see that bottom floor right there, looking right at you.

Okay, so these are two different views of the cube that I've drawn. I am actually going to return to these pictures in a few minutes, because I want us to look at them very closely. Remember the life lesson, which is to look at things very, very closely, and we're going to return to these. Anyway, though, that's the three-dimensional cube, but of course, how do you really produce a three-dimensional cube for real? You don't draw a picture of it; you actually build one. How do you do it? You take the square, the two-dimensional version of the cube, and what do you do?

Well, now we really see the pattern. We take it, we put it on the mathematical inkpad, we ink the whole thing up, and what do we do? We drag it in a perpendicular, new direction. I am going to drag it now in a perpendicular, new direction. Here we go, sweep it out, and you can see what I'm doing. I am producing the usual, three-dimensional cube that we are used to seeing, and here's the model. This model is what we get, then, after we have swept this out. Now, you can see the progression again, and we have the cube.

Now, we come to the interesting part. How do we build a four-dimensional cube? Well, we just continue the process. What would that mean? It would mean that I would take this three-dimensional cube, and do what to it? Well, I would ink it up, but notice that just with the square, I'm not just going to ink up the boundary. What did we ink up with the square? We inked up the entire inside. We put the entire inside on that inkpad, and then dragged it out and it left that residue that made the cube. How do we make a four-dimensional cube, then? I take this cube and do what to it?

I ink it up, but it's not just the kind of inking that we have done all our lives. It's not just a matter of inking up the faces of the cube. We really have to ink up every single point, even inside the cube. Here's how I sometimes think of it. I imagine the cube as being a kind of "cubular" sponge, and I'm literally going to put ink at every single point, even inside of it. Imagine now, then, that it's all inked up, and if you were to touch it, it would be a huge mess up, but I'll do it, because it's for the good of education.

You pick it up, and what are you going to do? We are going to drag it one unit in a perpendicular direction. Now, this is a problem, because we already saw in the previous lecture that in fact, I can't point to a direction that is simultaneously perpendicular to all of the three that we are used to. Let me just act it out, then, and then we'll understand this is not going to be quite perfect.

Here we go, though. Watch me as I take this, it's inked up, and remember, it's going to leave a residue, and I drag it and stop. One unit. I'll do it again. I take the cube, and imagine it's inked up, so watch the trail, and I'm going to move it one unit, and stop. That entire process, that motion, is, in fact, a four-dimensional cube.

What would it look like? Well, I actually built one for you, and so here it is. This is a four-dimensional cube, and I want us to study that a little bit, but now, the three-dimensional cube has certainly served its purpose, and I want us to look at this. Notice that this is exactly what I advertised. If I put my hands here, you can see a regular cube in between my hands. There's a regular cube there, and then I dragged it, and then the regular cube moved to here. What I see here, then, is a cube that has been dragged and then stopped, one unit; one unit later.

Well, this is a beautiful image of a four-dimensional cube, but you look at this image, and you say, "Wow, Ed, I can't believe you made that," and I did, but the point is that it seems complicated, and it certainly doesn't look like the cubes that we are used to. For example, if you look at the cubes that we are used to—here's just a small version of one that we can just look at and enjoy without dominating the entire table here—all the angles are right angles. All the sides have the same length. Everything seems to be the same. This is a little bit frustrating, then, that this doesn't have that shape at all. How can we come to grips with this potential problem?

Well, the answer is to return to these pictures that I advertised earlier. Let's take a look at these pictures. What are these? These are actually two-dimensional renderings of a three-dimensional object. This is the object that I was actually trying to produce for you, but of course that required all three dimensions. I'd not only have to go this way and this way, but I would have to come out to give it the depth. On the surface of a piece of paper, which is two-dimensional, of course, we know that I don't have that depth, so how do I capture that? Well, we just take it for granted. We don't even think about it. I produced a perspective drawing, so that, in fact, both of these are perspective drawings of the cube. We look at that with our three-dimensional eyeballs, and we say, "Ah, yes, Ed is quite a good artist. He captured the cube," and we see it, and we understand that there's depth involved.

Let's look at both of these images though with our naked eyes, where we just rawly look at what we see exactly, and not trying to interpret it. If we at this, in both of these images, we see something very strange. First of all, we see that in fact, these edges are crossing each other. Notice that they cross right here and here. They cross each other. We are looking at them, now, literally, just as literal figures.

Additionally, notice that this length does not seem nearly as long as this length, and with squares, of course, in cubes, all the sides are supposed to be the same. Notice that this angle right here is a very, very tiny angle, and this angle right here is a huge angle, and we know that all the angles are supposed to be 90 degrees, so we have this crisscrossing effect. That's wrong for a cube. Here's a cube, by the way. We know the angles are all supposed to be 90 degrees; they're not, and we also know that all the lengths are supposed to be equal, and they're sure far from that as well.

In fact, now you look back at this, and you say, "You know what, Ed? That was a lousy drawing." It's a lousy literal drawing. That's correct, but when we look at it in perspective, all of a sudden, the cube jumps out at us from the page. Similarly, here, you can see how tiny that floor is, when in fact, it is supposed to be the same length. These angles are all supposed to be 90 degrees, but we see that when we look at it in perspective.

Well, it turns out that this is a three-dimensional photograph of a four-dimensional cube. It is precisely the analog of this picture right here. I've taken, here, the square, and I've dragged it, and you can see all those crossing lines, and so forth. Here, I've taken the cube, and I have dragged it, and so all these lines that seem to be passing through itself, and the other sides and the edges, so that it seems like it is sort of inside itself, is the analog of these lines crossing themselves. In reality, if we had this sitting in four-dimensional space, it would look just as beautiful as this, in the sense that every side would be one unit long. Every angle would, in fact, be a 90-degree angle, and it all would look great, but we can't see that, since we are three-dimensional creatures, so instead, what we do is we draw, and examine, and explore, and enjoy a three-dimensional perspective photograph, the analog of this, to a four-dimensional cube.

Well, of course, the process can be continued. For example, suppose, now, for some perverse reason, that you wanted a five-dimensional cube. Well, now, we are all expert at what we need to do. What do you do? You take this beautiful but very complex four-dimensional object, and what do you do? You ink it up, and you don't just ink it up along the sides, and you don't just ink it up along the inside, you ink along all the four-dimensional inside of it, so that all of its guts get inked up, and what do we do? We drag it one unit in a new direction, perpendicular, so, I can't point to it, of course. I can't even point to the fourth one, but you can visualize doing that, and this motion can be set down into another perspective picture. Namely, take this entire image, move it to here, and then just indicate the drag lines, how the vertices, the corners, get moved, and those would produce the new edges. Just as we did with going from this cube to this cube, we see that the drag lines, these new edges appear, indicating one corner being glued and dragged to the other. These are the drag lines that we're seeing. You could build as high a dimensional cube as you wanted to without any problem at all.

In fact, once you have these models, you can actually see amazing patterns. Let me just show you a few, just for fun. The first pattern is: Let's just ask how many corners—in the math world, we call them vertices—there are on cubes. Where do we start? Should I start counting here? Of course not. That's far too complicated. We go back to the beginning.

Let's take a zero-dimensional cube, and ask how many vertices there are. Remember that the answer is always easy. There's just one thing there, so there's one vertex.

Now, what happened? We inked it up and we dragged it, and so now, how many vertices are there here, how many corners? You can see them marked in black. We've got one, and then one here. There are two. That kind of makes sense. I started with one here, with these guys, and then I dragged and stopped, and that gave me another one, so that I have these two.

Now, what about with the square? Well, with the square, you can visualize it. I have two corners here, and then when I drag it and stop, I get another two corners, so, in fact, here, I have four corners.

Okay, great. Now I take the square, which has four corners, and I'm going to drag it and stop. I get four more corners, so that now, I have eight corners.

Now, let's argue by analogy. What's really going on here? There's a pattern, right? How many corners does a particular dimensional cube have? Well, you take a look at how many corners the previous dimensional cube has, and what do you do? You just double it, because whatever number of vertices the, for example, three-dimensional cube has, when I drag it and stop, I get an exact replica of those vertices somewhere else. In fact, then, if I have so many vertices here, as with the square I have four vertices, I drag and stop, and I have four more vertices, so I double the four to get eight.

With the cube, I see that I have eight vertices, and what's your guess as to how many vertices I would have in a four-dimensional cube? Your guess might be, "Well, take eight and double it," and you'd get 16, and that's exactly how many vertices there are here, and you can see them. Between my hands, I have eight vertices, but notice that there are a lot of vertices untouched. In fact, how many? Precisely as many as there are on this cube, and so, there are eight more, and so we see 16. You can actually now go through and count this object if you want to, and check for 16, but it's easy to miss some, so it's better to think about the thing systematically, and look for a pattern.

Now, what other things could you count? Well, in fact, now you could actually say, "How many vertices would there be on a five-dimensional cube?" Now, we see the pattern. What do we do? Well, since we know that there are 16 here, how many vertices are there on a five-dimensional cube? You just take these vertices and double them, because we're going to drag, and so we have 16 and 16, or 32.

You can do the same kind of process if you want to by looking at the edges, and you can count edges in the same kind of way. In fact, you can think about how to count the edges. All you have to do is to say that you have all of the edges that you had in the previous cube, which means that in this case, we have all the edges of the regular cube here, and then I have another copy of those edges here. All the edges are there, and then we have some extra edges that we haven't even counted yet, those drag lines that actually made up the dragging into the extra dimension. How many of those new drag lines are there? Well, those drag lines are actually the drags of the vertices, so that in fact, if you wanted to figure out how many edges this thing has, all you have to do is take the number of edges of the cube one dimension below it, double it so that you get these, and then, you have to add the number of vertices of the lower dimensional cube to give you those new edges, and that would actually reveal the pattern for how to count the edges.

All the objects, therefore, on these cubes can be counted, and in fact, they can be counted in a simple way by just starting off with the zero-dimensional cube, and looking for a pattern. Quite often in life, then, when we see something, it seems so complex. If someone just gave this to us, we would have no idea how to look at it, how to count it, how to even perceive it, but by starting off simply, arguing by analogy, and looking for a pattern, we actually can then come to understand and see this in a more refined way.

Well, the one flaw of this beautiful perspective drawing is that not all the angles are right angles, not all the lengths are the same, the same flaws as we had with this image right here. Wouldn't it be wonderful, then, if I could actually produce for you a perfect four-dimensional cube in three space, where all the angles are right angles, all sides have the same length, and everything is perfect, and all is well with the world?

Well, we know we can't do that, because that requires four degrees of different directions, and we don't have that, but we can do something that actually captures that. How can we do it? Well, we don't look at this piece right now, because that's a little bit too complicated. Instead, we look at an easier question. Let's try to ask ourselves, "How could I capture, on the face of a piece of paper, a two-dimensional space, a regular three-dimensional cube where all the angles are perfect, and all the lengths are the same?"

It seems impossible, because of the perspective problem, but here's the trick. The trick is take the cube, and I'm going to try do this right now live, which, by the way, might be easier said than done, and actually unfold the cube. Now, what happens if we unfold the cube? If we unfold the cube, let's see what image we produce.

Now, on the plane and the surface of this two-dimensional tabletop, look what we have. The cube fits perfectly along here, and notice that every angle, in fact, is a right angle, and all the faces are perfect squares, just as they're supposed to be, so this looks really great.

Of course, it's not a cube, but what do I have to do? Well, what I have to do is pick up this object that resides in two-dimensional space, and take features of it, and fold it back onto itself in this extra degree of freedom, the space above. I have it wrapped around, and so what I really need to do is tell you how to glue up all these different edges to the other edges. In particular, for example, you can see that this edge right here needs to be glued up to some other edge, and which edge is it? Well, if you'll visualize picking this up, and now taking that edge and picking that up, what you see is that these two edges have to be glued together, so in fact, these two edges right here need to be glued together.

Similarly, we can mark off and say that this edge needs to be glued to this edge, and we can go through the whole object and do it. Maybe I will just do a few; this edge would be glued to this edge, this edge here would be glued to this edge here. This edge right here, well, if you just visualize it, where does that get glued to? That is going to get glued back to this edge right here. It has come back on this side. The real tricky ones, in fact, are these edges right here. Where would this edge—I'll call it a "question mark" edge—go? It's not obvious, but if you follow that edge very carefully and lift it up, and glue these two together, what do we see? We see that the "question mark" edge should go right to the top edge, so in fact, that "question mark" edge goes right to here, and similarly, this "question mark" edge here goes to this edge right here.

Now, armed with this cross-like structure, and the instructions as to how to assemble it, we actually have a perfect cube, a perfect cube, that in fact, is sitting on the plane perfectly, but instruction and assembly is required to make a perfect cube.

Well, what's the analog of this cross-like shape if we were to unfold a four-dimensional cube? If we would unfold this four-dimensional cube, in fact, what would we see? Well, that is sort of hard, because what are the boundaries of a four-dimensional cube?

Well, let's argue by analogy. The boundaries of a one-dimensional cube were, in fact, the zero-dimensional points. The boundaries of a two-dimensional cube are, in fact, the one-dimensional line segments around. The boundaries of a three-dimensional cube are the two-dimensional faces, like the two-dimensional faces of a die. Arguing by analogy, what would the boundary of a four-dimensional cube be? Three-dimensional cube. The boundary of a four-dimensional cube, then, is made up of three-dimensional cubes. How many are there? Well, you can actually count them. I'll try to count them for you right now. I'm going to show you all the three-dimensional cubes that are, in fact, in this artist's rendition of a cube. Let's see if you can see them.

Here's one, of course. This regular cube between my hands, so look between my hands. There's one. Then, there's this other that looks like a regular cube. There's no doubt about it. That's a regular cube between my two hands, so that's two. Now, let's see if we can find some other ones. Well, in fact, look at this squashed perspective cube that is in between my hands. It's a squashed cube. It's like a cube that I squashed down. You see it? That cube squashed down is another different cube. I haven't counted that one yet, so that's a third one. Then, I have a cube way over here that's the same type of squashed cube. That squashed cube right there is the fourth one. Then I have a cube right here squashed down. That's the fifth one. Then, I have a cube right here. That's a sixth one. Then, I have a cube right here. That's a seventh one. Then, I have one last cube right here, squashed down here. That's the eighth one. In fact, then, there are eight cubular faces to this four-dimensional cube.

If we were to somehow unfold this in the third dimension, what would we see? What we would see would be eight cubes that would be forming a shape of this sort. What would it look like? It would be exactly this shape right here.

Now, let's just make sure that we see that, in fact, this shape really comprises eight cubes, so let's count the cubes and make sure that we really do have eight. Well, we have one right here; two, then we have three, four, five, six, seven. Uh-oh. Well, there should be an extra cube somewhere. Do you see where it is? Well, no, you can't see where it is, but you know where it is. It's actually right inside, between this waistband of cubes. There's a cube in there. Look back here, and see that now, that comes into focus. If we were two-dimensional creatures on the table here, we would never see that square. That square is actually blocked from sight, but is surrounded by the waistline of these squares, similarly here, so that's the eighth one, and now, the gluing instructions are not along edges, but faces. This face gets glued to that face, so we have to bring them together. This face gets glued to that face, and you can figure out the corresponding image of this.

The beautiful thing about this image, by the way, besides the fact that every length is one unit and every angle is 90 degrees, so that it is a perfect four-dimensional cube, but unfolded, is that it really captures the spirit of a four-dimensional cube, but in our space, and in fact, actually was the inspiration for a very famous work about art by Salvador Dali. In his work, called *Corpus Hypercubicus*, what we actually see is the figure on the crucifix. And what we see here is a representation, in some sense, of the fourth dimension capturing a religious motif, that somehow, maybe Jesus is being thought of as an extra degree of freedom, or somehow, in a religious context. When you look at that image, though, which you see is an unfolded four-dimensional cube, trying to extend the usual notion of the usual cross. Again, then, through mathematics we see even the art world in a more powerful way.

Well, I wanted to close by just making a couple of other remarks, and maybe giving one more example, since it is sort of fun to build these things. I hate to remove this, because I just sort of love it, but I don't know where to put it. I just can't remove it, because I spent so much time making it.

Let's try to make one of the simplest objects that we can, very quickly, which would be like a pyramid, which is actually called, in the business, a tetrahedron. A tetrahedron is really just a pyramid where every face is a triangle. It is actually the simplest geometric solid that we can think of. Let's build one right now for fun. Where do you start? You start with zero-dimensional space, so do you know what a zero-dimensional tetrahedron is? Of course you do. It's a point, because everything is a point in zero-dimensional space. It couldn't be easier.

Now, how do you build triangles? Well, the way you build triangles, and here's the process, is that you take another copy of a point; you just take another point. Imagine it right here, and then just connect this new point to the previous picture. In this case, it's so simple. If I connect this to this picture, we just get a line segment, and indeed, we get this. Notice that all I did here was to take my old zero-dimensional triangle, or tetrahedron, and I just connected it with a new point, and it's made here.

Now what do I do? To get a two-dimensional tetrahedron, also known as a triangle, I take a new point, put it out there, and take that point and connect it to all the previous points. Do you see how I do that? What I get, in fact, is a triangle. In the math world, we call this a *cone*, we cone over this object.

How do I get a three-dimensional triangle, or a three-dimensional tetrahedron? I put it like this. I put this one above, and what do I do? I cone over each of the vertices and when I do that, what do I make? I actually make this triangular pyramid, so this is a three-dimensional tetrahedron.

How do you make a four-dimensional tetrahedron? Now, there's no problem. What do you do? It's hard to visualize it, but you just take another point in four-dimensional space, which, of course, I can't really capture, and what do you do? You cone over, or connect it to every single vertex on the previous one. The image, in fact, would look something like this. This is, then, a perspective three-dimensional "photograph," if you will, of a four-dimensional tetrahedron, and notice that I have this vertex up here, and I have just coned down to every one of the vertices, and so there is an example of that.

Well, just by arguing by analogy, what we see here is a powerful way of looking at not only our world, but in fact worlds that remain invisible, and the beauty of this type of thinking is that we can take ideas, issues, and concepts that seem so foreign, so removed, and are literally invisible to us, and make those things not only come into focus, but in some sense, we can begin to build intuition. We have a sense of how to build things, what things would look like, how many vertices would come out of them, and so forth, just by arguing by analogy.

Anyway, I hope that this journey of these past two lectures really captures the imagination of people, and that you will go on and think about the fourth dimension, and realize how dramatic it actually is. I teach a course at Williams College designed for humanities students, and we actually discuss the fourth dimension there. It actually inspired a student to write a limerick, which I wanted to close with, and share with you, when you look at these cubes, and how they are sort of hanging there in this extension, I just wanted to share with you this student limerick from Williams College:

A cube in the fourth dimension

Is really too strange to mention,

So I took Math 180.

The concepts were weighty,

But now I look at cubes in extension.

It's a wonderful way to open the mind all through the power of arguing by analogy and looking at simple things deeply.

Timeline

30,000 B.C. ....Palaeolithic peoples in central Europe and France recorded numbers on bones.

3000 B.C. ....The abacus was in use in the Middle East and around the Mediterranean. A different sort of abacus was in use in China.

2000 B.C. ....Babylonians developed a base-60 counting system with extensive calculational capabilities.

540 B.C. ....Pythagoras founded his school and proved the Pythagorean theorem.

387 B.C. ....Plato founded the Academy.

300 B.C. ....Euclid presented the axiomatic method in geometry in his *Elements*.

225 B.C. ....Apollonius described the geometry of conic sections.

A.D. 150.....................................Ptolemy had many important results in geometry. His theories in astronomy were accepted for the next 1000 years.

1200 ....Fibonacci brought knowledge of Islamic mathematics to Italy.

1336 ....At the University of Paris, mathematics was made a mandatory subject for a degree.

1489 ....The first appearance of + and − signs occurred in an arithmetic book in German by Widman.

1500 ....Leonardo da Vinci kept extensive notebooks of his interests in mathematics, anatomy, engineering, and art, among other topics.

1827	Möbius's work on analytical geometry, *Der barycentrische Calkul*, became a classic and included many of his results on projective and affine geometry.
1854	George Boole developed Boolean logic in *Laws of Thought*.
1874	Cantor invented set theory.
1879	Kempe published his "proof" of the four-color theorem.
1881	Used in set theory, Venn introduced his *Venn diagrams*.
1900	Hilbert posed 23 problems at the Second International Congress of Mathematicians in Paris as a challenge for the 20th century. Many have been solved to date; they are considered milestones.
1905	Einstein published his simple, elegant special theory of relativity.
1913	Ramanujan first wrote Hardy from India.
1936	Turing developed the concept of a Turing Machine.
1970	Mandelbrot coined the term *fractal*.
1976	Appel and Haken showed that the four- color conjecture is true using 1200 hours of computer time to examine about 1500 configurations.
1995	Andrew Wiles, with help from Richard Taylor, published a rigorous proof of Fermat's last theorem.

Glossary

Algorithm: A recipe or procedure for solving a problem in a finite number of steps.

Barnsley's fern: A natural-looking, fern-like fractal that can be created by a simple collage method process, created by Michael Barnsley.

Borromean rings: A configuration of three rings with the property that, if any one of them is removed, the other two can be separated, but with all three present, they are inseparable.

Brownian Motion: A phenomenon of random movement, such as particles in fluid.

Buffon's Needle: Buffon's Needle refers to the experiment of dropping a needle randomly on a lined piece of paper, where the needle is as long as the distance between the lines. The probability that the needle lands on a line gives a way to compute π using randomness.

Common factor: Given two integers a and b, a common factor is an integer k such that k divides evenly into both a and b.

Conic sections: The conic sections are the parabola, ellipse (which includes the circle), and the hyperbola. These are known as conic sections because they are formed by the intersection of a plane with a cone.

Dimension: One of the degrees of freedom in space. For example, a line has one dimension, a plane two, and a room appears to have three dimensions.

Duality: Two objects exhibit duality if higher-dimensional features of one correspond to lower dimensional features of the other and vice versa. For example, the cube and octahedron exhibit duality, because the number of vertices of the cube equals the number of faces of the octahedron and vice versa.

Euler characteristic: Given a graph or doodle, the Euler characteristic is the number $V-E+F$, where V is the number of vertices, E is the number of edges, and F is the number of faces. For any connected drawing in the plane or on a sphere, the Euler characteristic always equals 2.

Expected value: The average net gain or loss that one would expect if a given probabilistic event occurred many times.

Fair game: A game where the expected value is zero.

Fibonacci numbers: Members of the Fibonacci sequence.

Fibonacci sequence: The sequence of numbers starting with 1, 1, where each subsequent number is the sum of the previous two. Written as a recursive formula, the nth Fibonacci number $F_n = F_{n-1} + F_{n-2}$. So the Fibonacci sequence begins: 1, 1, 2, 3, 5, 8, 13, 21, 34, ...

Focus (foci): The foci of an ellipse are the two fixed points such that the ellipse is the set of all points such that the sum of the distances to the two foci is a fixed given value.

Fractal: An infinitely detailed pattern or picture with the quality of self-similarity; on any scale the shape resembles itself.

Geometry: The branch of mathematics that studies the visual world and abstractions of it such as lines, angles, points, surfaces, and solids.

Hypotenuse: In a right triangle, the side that does not meet the right angle.

Integer: A whole number (positive, zero, or negative); ...-2, -1, 0, 1, 2...

Irrational numbers: A real number that is not rational. Examples: π and the square root of 2.

Iterate: To repeat.

Klein Bottle: An elegant one-sided surface formed by connecting the two ends of a cylinder in such a way that the resulting solid has no inside or outside. It can only be portrayed in three-dimensional space by introducing a self-intersection. It can be drawn completely in four-dimensional space.

Koch curve: A self-similar fractal that is infinitely jagged and has infinite length.

Logarithm: The exponent to which a base must be raised in order to produce a given number. For example, if the base is 10, then the logarithm of 1000 is 3, because $10^3 = 1000$.

Lucas sequence: The sequence formed with the same rule as the Fibonacci sequence, only starting with the first two numbers as 2 and 1. The first few terms in the Lucas sequence are 2, 1, 3, 4, 7, 11, 18, 29, 47, …

Menger sponge: A self-similar fractal in 3-dimensional space formed by a sculptural collage iterative algorithm that involves replacing a cube by 20 smaller cubes.

Möbius band: A surface having only one side, constructed by inserting a half-twist into a cylindrical band.

Natural numbers: The positive whole numbers: 1, 2, 3…

Newcomb's paradox: A paradoxical situation where an individual is given a choice between one box of money or two boxes of money. The specifics of the situation make each decision appear correct, even though they are opposite decisions.

Orientability: The quality of a surface of being able to have a sense of clockwise that is consistent over the whole surface.

Perfect number: A number that equals the sum of its factors. For example, $6 = 1+2+3$.

Planar objects: Objects that can exist in the plane. For example, a square is a planar object, while a cube is not.

Plane: Sometimes called the Cartesian plane, the flat space that consists of the set of all points with two coordinates (x, y).

Platonic solids: The five solids whose faces are congruent, regular polygons and each of whose vertices has the same number of incident edges. The Platonic or regular solids are the tetrahedron, cube, octahedron, dodecahedron, and icosahedron.

Polygon: A closed curve that is made from a finite number of straight line segments.

Probability: A fraction between zero and one that describes how likely an event is. For events with equally likely outcomes, it equals the quotient of favorable outcomes to possible outcomes.

Pythagorean theorem: In a right triangle, the square of the length of the hypotenuse is equal to the sum of the squares of the lengths of the other two sides.

Pythagorean triangle: A right triangle with integer-length sides, for example, a 3, 4, 5 triangle.

Rational numbers: A number that can be written as a quotient of integers, with a nonzero integer in the denominator.

Real numbers: All the decimal numbers, which together comprise the real line.

Regular solids: Synonymous with Platonic solids.

Sierpinski carpet: The fractal resulting from an iterative, collage process that starts with a square and repeatedly replaces the collage at each stage with eight reduced copies surrounding a central square to produce the collage of collages at the next stage.

Sierpinski triangle: A self-similar two-dimensional shape formed by a fractal algorithm involving replacing a triangle with three triangles.

St. Petersburg paradox: Suppose a fair coin is tossed, and you receive $2 if it lands heads up for the first time on the first flip, $4 if it lands heads up for the first time on the second flip, $8 if it lands heads up for the first time on the third flip, and so on. The expected value of this game is infinite, yet how much would you pay to play?

Symmetry: A symmetry of a figure is a rigid motion of the figure or shape that results in the figure looking the same as before the motion. For example, rotating an equilateral triangle by 120 degrees is a symmetry of the triangle.

Tangent: A line is tangent to a circle or a sphere if it just grazes it, touching at one point only.

Topology: The branch of mathematics that studies properties of shapes and solids that are unchanged by elastic motions, like twisting or stretching. For example, an inner tube and the surface of a doughnut are topologically equivalent.

Torus: A surface having the shape of the boundary of a doughnut.

Turing Machine: An abstract machine, conceptually analogous to a computer program. Fed a tape, the machine reads the tape, one entry at a time, erases the entry, and prints an output based on a finite list of rules.

Vertex (vertices): In a geometrical object with edges and faces, a vertex is a point at the end of an edge. For example in a regular solid, the vertices are the points where the edges come together.

Zeckendorff decomposition: Writing an integer uniquely as the sum of Fibonacci numbers.

π: Greek letter denoting the value 3.1415926… equal to the ratio of the circumference of a circle to its diameter.

Biographical Notes

Cantor, Georg (1845–1918). Cantor was born in Denmark but spent most of his childhood in St. Petersburg, Russia. At age 11, his family moved to Germany, where he remained for much of his life. He completed his dissertation in number theory in 1867. Later, he developed the notions of set theory and precise notions of infinity, including the concept of different-sized infinite collections. He suffered from bouts of depression and mental illness and eventually died in a sanatorium. Combined with the fact that many of his ideas were not accepted by the mathematical community of his day, Cantor is a somewhat tragic figure in mathematics.
http://www-gap.dcs.st-
and.ac.uk/~history/Mathematicians/Cantor.html
http://dbeveridge.web.wesleyan.edu/wescourses/2001f/chem160/01/
Who's percent20Who/georg_cantor.htm

da Vinci, Leonardo (1452–1519). At the age of 15, Leonardo moved to Florence to become an apprentice under the artist Andrea del Verrocchio. He kept highly detailed notebooks on subjects as varied as anatomy and hydraulics, as well as artistic sketches. Much of what we know of his life today is from these notebooks, as well as tax records. In 1495, he began painting *The Last Supper*. When Fra Luca Pacioli, the famous mathematician, moved to Milan, the two became friends, and da Vinci began to develop his interest in mathematics. In 1502, he left Milan to begin work as a military engineer and became acquainted with Niccolo Macchiavelli. He returned to Milan in 1506, where he became involved in hydrodynamics, anatomy, mechanics, mathematics, and optics. It is estimated that he worked on the *Mona Lisa* around 1505.

Escher, Maurits Cornelius (1898–1972). Dutch graphic artist. Although his family attempted to steer him toward a path of architecture, Escher struggled and eventually felt that a graphic arts program was a better fit. Encouraged by Samuel Jesserum de Mesquita, he experimented with woodcutting designs and printing techniques. Several times throughout his career, Escher involved himself with mathematicians. Unable to quite grasp the abstractions, he processed their work on an artistic level. Polya's paper on plane symmetry groups was quite influential. Escher later became friends with Coxeter and incorporated Coxeter's work on hyperbolic tessellations into several pieces. He achieved world fame over the course of his lifetime.

http://www-gap.dcs.st-
and.ac.uk/~history/Mathematicians/Escher.html
http://www.cs.ualberta.ca/~tegos/escher/biography/

Euclid (c. 325 B.C.–265 B.C.). Mathematician of Alexandria, Egypt. Very little is known of Euclid's life, other than his major achievement, *Elements*, a compilation of 13 books. In it, much basic geometry and number theory is built up using the axiomatic method; beginning with definitions and five postulates, Euclid then rigorously proves each statement as a result of previous statements. Much of it remains central to the study of mathematics today. In the 19th century, the parallel postulate was reinvestigated: that "one and only one line can be drawn through a point parallel to a given line." Dropping this condition led to the development of non-Euclidean geometries.

http://www-gap.dcs.st-
and.ac.uk/~history/Mathematicians/Euclid.html
http://www.lib.virginia.edu/science/parshall/euclid.html

Euler, Leonhard (1707–1783). Swiss mathematician and scientist. Euler was the student of Jean Bernoulli. He was professor of medicine and physiology and later became a professor of mathematics at St. Petersburg. Euler is the most prolific mathematical author of all time, writing on mathematics, acoustics, engineering, mechanics, and astronomy. He introduced standardized notations, many now in modern use, and contributed unique ideas to all areas of analysis, especially in the study of infinite series. He lost nearly all his sight by 1771 and was the father of 13 children.

Fermat, Pierre de (1601–1665). French lawyer and judge in Toulouse, enormously talented amateur mathematician. He worked in number theory, geometry, analysis, and algebra and was the first developer of analytic geometry, including the discovery of equations of lines, circles, ellipses, parabolas, and hyperbolas. He wrote Introduction to Plane and Solid Loci and formulated the famed "Fermat's Last Theorem," as a note in the margin of his copy of Bachet's edition of Diophantus's *Arithmetica*. He developed a procedure for finding maxima and minima of functions through infinitesimal analysis, essentially by the limit definition of derivative, and applied this technique to many problems including analyzing the refraction of light.

Fibonacci, Leonardo (c. 1175–1250). Italian mathematician, the "greatest European mathematician of the Middle Ages." He began as a merchant, like his father, a customs officer. This afforded the opportunity for Fibonacci to learn calculational techniques, including Hindu-Arabic numerals, not yet in use in Europe. He later traveled extensively throughout the Mediterranean coast, returning to Pisa around 1200. For the next 25 years, he worked on his mathematical compositions, of which five books have survived to modern times. He is best known for the sequence that bears his name.
http://www.mcs.surrey.ac.uk/Personal/R.Knott/Fibonacci/fibBio.html
http://www.lib.virginia.edu/science/parshall/fibonacc.html

Gauss, Carl Friedrich (1777–1855). German mathematician; commonly considered the world's greatest mathematician, hence known as the Prince of Mathematicians. He was professor of astronomy and director of the Observatory at Göttingen. He provided the first complete proof of the fundamental theorem of algebra and made substantial contributions to geometry, algebra, number theory, and applied mathematics. He established mathematical rigor as the standard of proof. His work on the differential geometry of curved surfaces formed an essential base for Einstein's general theory of relativity.

Kepler, Johannes (1571–1630). German astronomer and mathematician; mathematician and astrologer to Emperor Rudolph II (in Prague). Kepler assisted Tycho Brahe (the Danish astronomer) in compiling the best collection of astronomical observations in the pretelescope era. He developed three laws of planetary motion and made the first attempt to justify them mathematically. They were later shown to be a consequence of the universal law of gravitation by Newton, applying the new techniques of calculus.

Mandelbrot, Benoit (1924–). Born in Warsaw, Poland, Mandelbrot's family emigrated to France when he was 11, where his uncle began introducing him to mathematical concepts. He earned his Ph.D. from the University of Paris in 1952, on a mathematical analysis of the distribution of words in the English language. In 1967, he published, "How long is the coast of Britain?" Its title illustrates the phenomenon in which an object's perimeter may have undeterminable length; the measurements vary with the scale of the

ruler, so to speak. Mandelbrot coined the term *fractal* in the mid-1970s to describe certain self-similar patterns, including the famous *Mandelbrot set*. These patterns were exploited by screen-saver programmers in the latter half of the 1990s, hypnotizing the baby-boom generation with psychedelic visuals, the likes of which had not been seen since the 1960s. Mandelbrot became professor of mathematics at Yale University in 1987.
http://www.fractovia.org/people/mandelbrot.html

Möbius, August (1790–1868). German mathematician and astronomer. He studied astronomy under several heavily mathematically inclined teachers, including Karl Mollweide, Gauss, and Johann Pfaff. Möbius contributed in analytical geometry and developed ideas that would later contribute to projective geometry and topology. He was a professor of astronomy at the University of Leipzig and observer at the Observatory, also at Leipzig. The Möbius strip is a one-sided object, which Möbius himself did not invent; however, he did describe other polyhedra with this property, and he introduced the related concept of orientability.
http://scienceworld.wolfram.com/biography/Moebius.html
http://www-gap.dcs.st-and.ac.uk/~history/Mathematicians/Mobius.html

Pascal, Blaise (1623–1662). French mathematician, scientist, and philosopher. Pascal started young and published his *Essay on Conic Sections* in 1640. He invented a digital calculator and was perhaps the second person to produce a mechanical device to help with arithmetic. He wrote scientific works concerning pressure and the vacuum. He is famous mathematically for contributing his name to Pascal's Triangle, which he wrote about and which is involved in the Binomial Theorem. He wrote a philosophical work *Pensées*, making him a rare individual who made significant contributions both to mathematics and philosophy.

Ramanujan, Srinivasa Aiyangar (1887–1920). Born in a small village southwest of Madras, Ramanujan was one of India's greatest mathematical geniuses. He was largely self-taught and gained a measure of recognition in the Madras area for his work in analytic number theory. He connected with the Western world in 1913 when he wrote Hardy, in England, and included a long list of mathematical results. His relative mathematical isolation produced the odd situation in which the compiled list contained many easy, well-known results side by side with startlingly important results. Hardy recognized his genius and arranged for Ramanujan to come to England in 1914. Ramanujan's next five years were the most productive of his life, although his health began to falter. He died of tuberculosis, within a year of returning to India.

http://home.att.net/~s-prasad/math.htm

http://www-gap.dcs.st-and.ac.uk/~history/Mathematicians/Ramanujan.html

Turing, Alan (1912–1954). Born in Paddington, London, Turing was educated at public schools, where he frustrated his teachers by his determination to follow his own ideas. He did excel in mathematics and read Einstein's papers on relativity on his own. Turing entered King's College, in Cambridge, to study mathematics. There, he developed his interest in mathematical logic. In 1936, he published *On Computable Numbers, with an application to the Entscheidungsproblem*. In this paper, he developed his best-known concept, now known as the Turing Machine. This is an abstract machine that is fed a tape. It reads the tape, one entry at a time, erases the entry, and prints an output based on a finite list of rules. It is more analogous to a computer program than to an actual computer.

Bibliography

Essential:

Burger, Edward B., and Michael Starbird. *The Heart of Mathematics: An invitation to effective thinking*. Emeryville, CA: Key College Publishing, ©2000. This award-winning book presents deep and fascinating mathematical ideas in a lively, accessible, and readable way. The review in the June-July 2001 issue of the *American Mathematical Monthly* says, "This is very possibly the best 'mathematics for the non-mathematician' book that I have seen—and that includes popular (non-textbook) books that one would find in a general bookstore." Much of the content of this Teaching Company course is treated in this book. http://www.heartofmath.com

Supplementary:

Abbott, Edwin. *Flatland: A Romance of Many Dimensions*. London: Dover Publications, 1884. For more than 100 years, this story of A. Square in two-dimensional Flatland has delighted readers of all ages. It is a story that takes place in a flat, two-dimensional world. It demonstrates mathematical concepts of dimensionality in the context of a parody of 19th-century English society and class structure.

Barnsley, Michael. *Fractals Everywhere,* Academic Press, San Diego, 2000. Michael Barnsley is one of the prominent contributors to the modern study of fractals. This textbook is a rather technical description of the mathematics behind the production of fractals. It includes many pictures of fractals and the equations that produce them as well as proofs of the mathematical theorems that underlie the study of the iterative function systems that produce life-like fractals.

Bell, E.T. *Men of Mathematics*. New York: Simon & Schuster, 1937. This book is a classic of mathematics history, filled with quotes and stories (often apocryphal) of famous mathematicians.

Blatner, David. *The Joy of π*. New York: Walker Publishing Company, 1997. This fun paperback is filled with gems and details about the history of the irrational number π.

Boyer, Carl B. *A History of Mathematics*. Princeton: Princeton University Press, 1968. This book is an extensive survey of the history of mathematics from earliest recorded history through the 19th century.

Cajori, Florian. *A History of Mathematics*, 5th ed. New York: Chelsea Publishing Company, 1991; 1st ed., 1893. This work provides a survey of the development of mathematics and the lives of mathematicians from ancient times through the end of World War I.

Calinger, Ronald. *A Contextual History of Mathematics*. Upper Saddle River, NJ: Prentice-Hall, 1999. This modern, readable text offers a survey of mathematics from the origin of number through the development of calculus and classical probability.

Davis, Donald M. *The Nature and Power of Mathematics*. Princeton: Princeton University Press, 1993. This wide-ranging book describes an array of ideas from all areas of mathematics, including brief biographies of Gauss and Kepler.

Dunham, William. *Journey through Genius: The Great Theorems of Mathematics*. New York: John Wiley & Sons, 1990. Each of this book's 12 chapters covers a great idea or theorem and includes a brief history of the mathematicians who worked on that idea.

Gies, Frances, and Joseph Gies. *Leonard of Pisa and the New Mathematics of the Middle Ages*. Gainesville, GA: New Classics Library, 1969. This book presents a look at Leonard Fibonacci and the town of Pisa in the 13th century. As mathematical knowledge from the Muslim world was brought in, the Western world saw the first new mathematical concepts since Euclid.

Hardy, G.H. *A Mathematician's Apology*. Cambridge University Press, 1942. The brilliant number theorist G.H. Hardy wrote this well-known classic. It is a memoir of his career, including the period in which Ramanujan touched his life. *A Mathematician's Apology* presents Hardy's vision of what "pure" mathematics is and how a person completely consumed by the quest for abstract mathematical insight feels about life and work.

Kanigel, Robert. *The Man Who Knew Infinity: A Life of the Genius Ramanujan*. Washington Square Press, 1991. This book is a delightful biography of one of the most brilliant mathematicians of modern times, Ramanujan. This well-documented but most readable account follows Ramanujan from the slums of India, through his time working with Hardy at Cambridge, to his early and tragic death at age 32.

Kline, Morris. *Mathematics: A Cultural Approach*. Reading, MA: Addison-Wesley Publishing Company, 1962. This survey of mathematics presents its topics in both historical and cultural settings, relating the ideas to the contexts in which they developed.

Livio, Mario. *The Golden Ratio: The Story of Phi, the World's Most Astonishing Number*. New York: Broadway Books, 2002. This book is written for the layperson and delves into the number Phi, also known as the Golden Ratio.

Scieszka, Jon, and Lane Smith (illustrator). *Math Curse*. New York: Viking Children's Books, 1995. This book is a fantastical children's story of a girl who wakes up one morning to perceive the world through a mathematical filter.

Stillwell, John, *Mathematics and Its History,* Springer, New York, 2002. This delightful book presents undergraduate level mathematics through its history as a means to unify disparate mathematical areas. Each chapter contains a biographical sketch of a mathematician and presents intriguing questions and mathematical insights in an historical context.

Tahan, Malba (translated by Leslie Clark and Alastair Reid). *The Man Who Counted: A Collection of Mathematical Adventures*. New York: W.W. Norton & Company, 1993. Originally published in Brazil in 1949, this book is a combination of clever mathematical puzzles woven through the adventures of a 13th-century Arabian mathematician.